D1219586

Molecular Biology
Biochemistry and Biophysics

Molekularbiologie
Biochemie und Biophysik

2

Springer-Verlag New York Inc. 1968

K. Freudenberg · A. C. Neish

Constitution and Biosynthesis of Lignin

With 10 Figures

Springer-Verlag New York Inc. 1968

Professor Dr. phil. Karl Freudenberg

Direktor emeritus des chemischen Instituts
der Universität Heidelberg

Arthur Charles Neish

Professor of Biology, Dalhousie University
Director, Atlantic Regional Laboratory, National Research Council of Canada
Halifax, Nova Scotia, Canada

Title No. 3802

Table of Contents

Monomeric Intermediates in the Biosynthesis of Lignin

ARTHUR C. NEISH, Halifax, Nova Scotia

I. Introduction 3

II. Experimental Methods 9

A. General Remarks 9

B. Tracer Studies 10

1. Feeding of Precursors 10

2. Measurement of ^{14}C-Incorporation into Lignin 12

C. Enzyme Studies 13

III. Biosynthesis of Aromatic Amino Acids in Plants 15

A. Summary of Work with Bacterial Mutants 15

B. Studies on Vascular Plants 15

IV. Ring-substituted Cinnamic Acids as Intermediates in Lignification . . . 17

A. General Remarks 17

B. Tracer Studies 17

1. Comparison of Precursors 17

2. Comparison of Species 29

C. Enzyme Studies 30

V. Cinnamyl-Alcohol Derivatives as Intermediates in Lignification 31

VI. Compounds Biogenetically-Related to Lignin 32

VII. Evolution of Lignification 34

VIII. Summary 37

IX. References 37

The Constitution and Biosynthesis of Lignin

KARL FREUDENBERG, Heidelberg

Part I

A. The Beginning 47

B. Lignin Preparations and Their Isolation 50

C. Lignin Derivatives and Their Preparation 53

D. The Aromatic Nature of Lignin 55

E. Other Observations 60
1. Liberation of Formaldehyde; search for C-Methyl 60
2. Oxidation to Vanillin and Allied Materials 61
3. Other Oxidation Products 62
4. Hydrogenation 62
5. Lignin and Alcohols 63

F. The Elemental Analysis of Lignin and the Calculation of Its Composition . 64
1. Introductory Remarks 64
2. Expression of Lignin Analyses 65
3. Recalculation of Analyses for Acetyllignin 66
4. Recalculation of Analyses for Methyllignin 67
5. Recalculation of Lignothioglycolic Acid 68

G. Analytical Data on Lignin 69
1. Elemental Composition 69
2. Hydroxyl Estimation 70
3. Carbonyl Groups 72
4. Ether Oxygen and Oxygen Balance 72

H. Early Approaches to the Constitution of Lignin 74

Part II

A. Degradation of Lignin to Methoxybenzenecarboxylic Acids and Other Products 78
1. Compounds of the Catechol (Veratrole) Series 78
2. Compounds of the Anisole Series 80
3. Compounds of the Trimethoxybenzene Series 80
4. Other Oxidation Products 80

B. The Dehydrogenation of Coniferyl Alcohol 82
1. Introductory Remarks 82
2. Monolignols 85
3. Dilignols 86
4. Trilignols 91
5. Higher Oligolignols 91

C. Linkage of Lignin with Carbohydrates 92

D. Quinone Methides: Benzyl Aryl Ethers in Lignin; Hydrolysis Products 93

E. Biochemical and Tracer Experiments 97
1. Biochemical Experiments and Other Observations 97
2. Tracer Experiments 99

F. Schematic Model of the Constitution of Spruce Lignin 102

G. Appraisal of the Schematic Formula for Spruce Lignin 105

H. Other Proposals for Formulae 108

I. Beech Lignin, Other Kinds of Lignin and the Concept of Lignin; Lignite and Humic Acid 110

1. Beech Lignin and Other Kinds of Lignin 110
2. The Concept of Lignin 114
3. Fossilized Wood (Lignite) 115
4. Humic Substances 115

K. Concluding Remark 116

L. References 116

Subject Index 123

Arthur C. Neish

Monomeric Intermediates in the Biosynthesis of Lignin

Table of Contents

I. Introduction 3

II. Experimental Methods 9
- A. General Remarks 9
- B. Tracer Studies 10
  - 1. Feeding of Precursors 10
  - 2. Measurement of ^{14}C-Incorporation into lignin 12
- C. Enzyme Studies 13

III. Biosynthesis of Aromatic Amino Acids in Plants 15
- A. Summary of Work with Bacterial Mutants 15
- B. Studies on Vascular Plants 15

IV. Ring-substituted Cinnamic Acids as Intermediates in Lignification 17
- A. General Remarks 17
- B. Tracer Studies 17
  - 1. Comparison of Precursors 17
  - 2. Comparison of Species 29
- C. Enzyme Studies 30

V. Cinnamyl-Alcohol Derivatives as Intermediates in Lignification 31

VI. Compounds Biogenetically-Related to Lignin 32

VII. Evolution of Lignification 34

VIII. Summary 37

IX. References 37

I. Introduction

Among terrestrial plants the vascular plants are the largest and the most conspicuous. Because of the presence of lignified supporting and conducting tissues such as xylem, terrestrial vascular plants can develop large upright forms. Composed mainly of xylem tissue, the stems of trees are characterized by elongated cells with thickened walls, impregnated by lignin. Diagrams of xylem cells (vessels, tracheids and fibers) can be seen in textbooks of plant anatomy (e.g. ESAU, 1953). A cross section of xylem tissue is shown in the section of this volume written by Professor FREUDENBERG (Fig. 1, p. 98). In general the occurrence of lignin in the plant kingdom is associated with the presence of these cells which comprise xylem. Thus lignin is found in vascular plants such as lycopods, ferns, gymnosperms and angiosperms, whereas it is absent from simple plants such as fungi, and from all other organisms. The mosses are an exceptional group which do not have the cells characteristic of xylem tissue but which contain lignin-like materials. These "moss lignins" have been discussed by Professor FREUDENBERG in this volume, and some doubts have been expressed as to whether or not they are true lignins (FR.* pp. 113—114).

Work on the chemistry of lignin indicates that it is a polymer derived from the phenylpropanoid compound, coniferyl alcohol and related alcohols. This chapter is a review of pertinent work on the biosynthesis of C_6C_3 (phenylpropanoid) units which can be used by plants for the formation of lignin. The mechanism of the dehydropolymerization of these units to lignin and the structure of lignin is discussed in this volume by Professor FREUDENBERG. The biochemical degradation of lignin by microorganisms is another interesting aspect of lignin biochemistry. This topic, which has been reviewed by FLAIG (1962) and NORD (1964), is considered to be outside the scope of this monograph.

A botanist recognizes lignin as a substance encrusting the walls of vascular and sclerenchyma cells, such as tracheids, vessels and fibers, and causing these cells to have special staining characteristics or to give specific color reactions. For example, the formation of a red color on treatment with a mixture of phloroglucinol and hydrochloric acid has long been used to detect lignin in plant materials. This reaction, which was discovered by WIESNER (1878), was explained by ADLER, BJÖRKVIST and HÄGGROTH (1948), 70 years later, as being due to condensation of the coniferyl aldehyde group in lignin. Another widely-used color test, discovered by MÄULE (1900), involves treating woody material in succession with dilute permanganate, hydrochloric acid and ammonia. The material is washed with water between each treatment. Wood from angiosperms gives a rose-red color, whereas gymnospermous

* FREUDENBERG.

woods give a brown color. A suggestion by GIBBS that the red coloration of the MÄULE test is correlated with the presence of syringyl groups in lignin was verified by the work of CREIGHTON, GIBBS and HIBBERT (1944); TOWERS (1951); and TOWERS and GIBBS (1953).

A major problem in studying the chemistry of lignin is the difficulty of isolating lignin from plant materials without having it undergo secondary reactions. Isolated lignins are usually given names such as Klason lignin, alkali lignin, ethanol lignin, etc., which indicate the method used in their preparation, since these substances all have different properties. The problem of obtaining lignin preparations suitable for chemical studies is discussed elsewhere in this volume (FR. pp. 50—53).

The term "protolignin" has been used for lignin as it exists in the plants, whereas the term "native lignin" has been used for a relatively small fraction of the protolignin which can be extracted with the neutral solvents such as ethanol (BRAUNS and BRAUNS, 1960). FREUDENBERG prefers to refer to these simply as "lignin" and "soluble lignin", respectively (FR. p. 52). In biochemical studies lignin has usually been recognized by simple aromatic degradation products, and KRATZL (1965) has listed lignin "criteria" which give some of the important degradation reactions used. Some of these are shown in Figs. 1, 2 and 3, which follow.

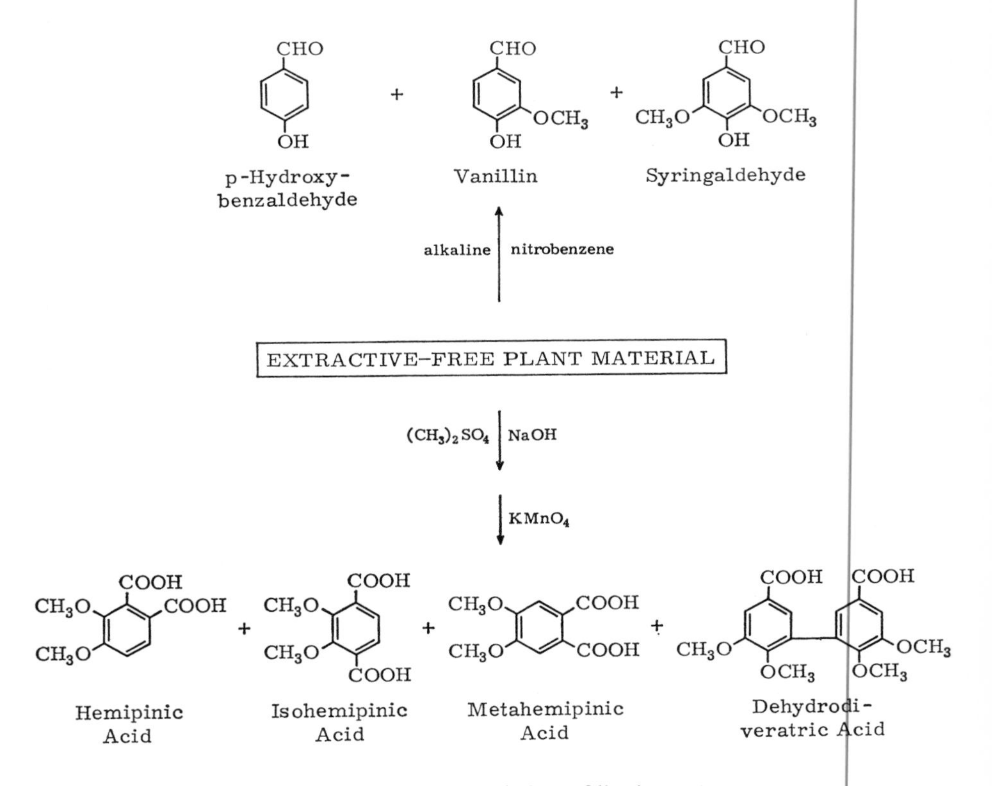

Fig. 1. Oxidative degradation of lignin *in situ*

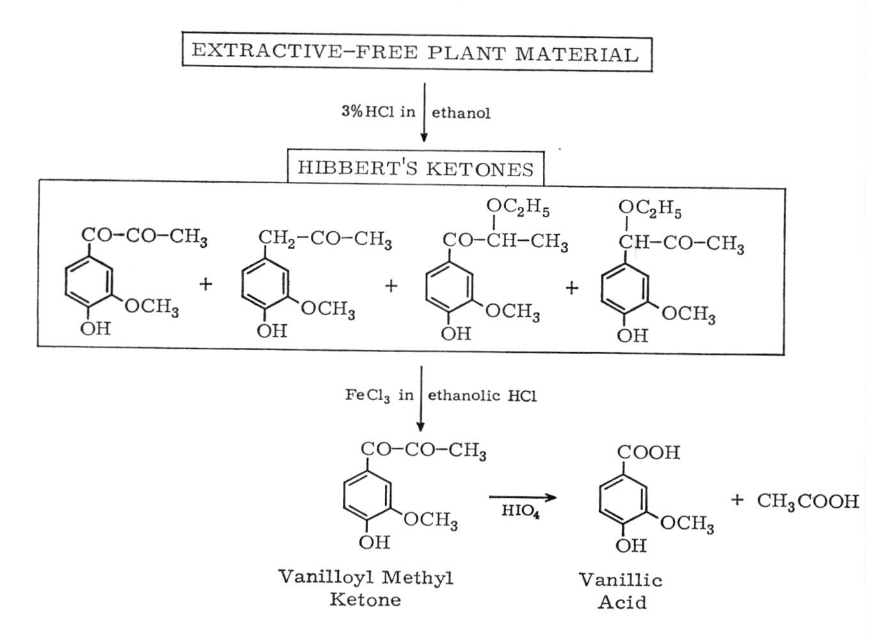

Fig. 2. Ethanolysis of spruce lignin. The corresponding syringyl derivatives are obtained from Angiosperms, along with the guaiacyl compounds shown in this figure

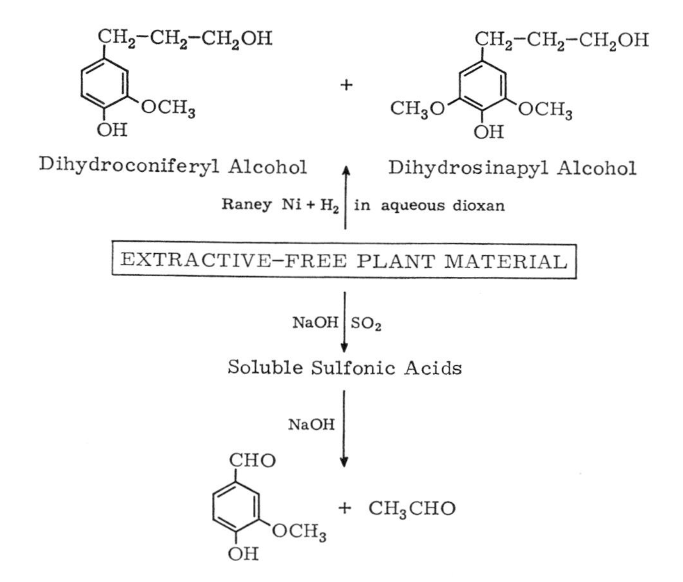

Fig. 3. Degradation of lignin by hydrogenolysis (Angiosperms) or alkaline hydrolysis of sulfonic acids (Gymnosperms)

Woody tissues have quite high lignin contents since they are composed to a large extent of tracheids, vessels and fibers. In herbaceous plants these elements are "diluted" by other cells, such as parenchyma cells, which do not have strongly

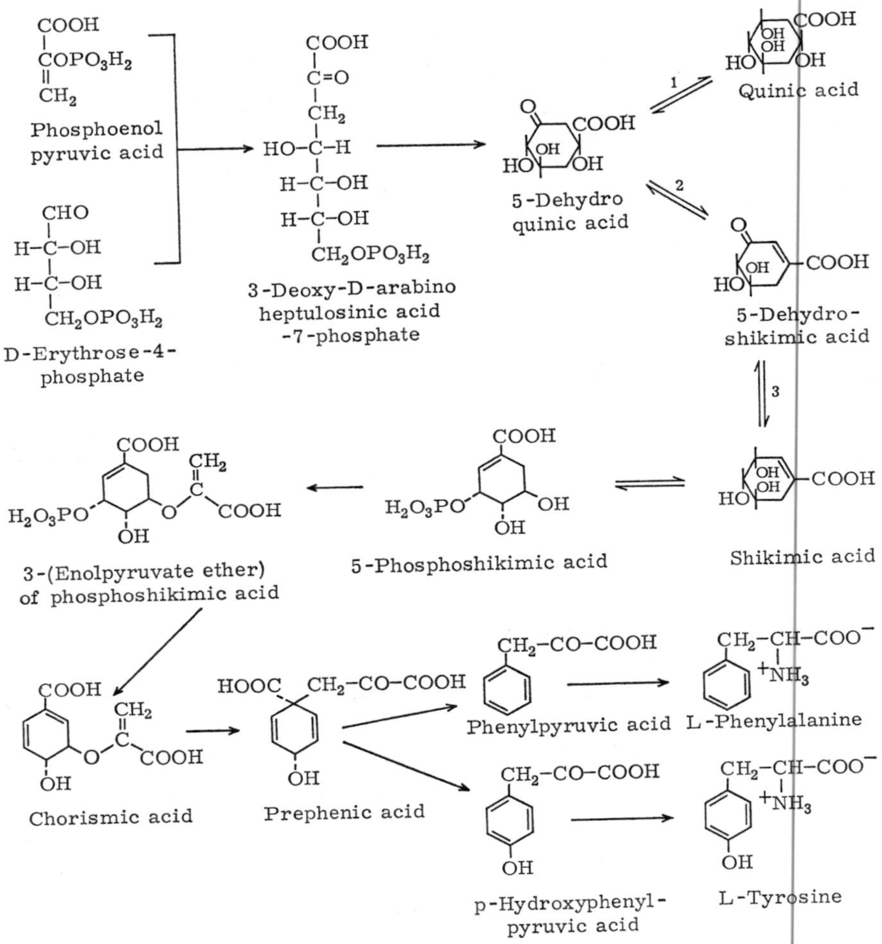

Fig. 4. Biosynthesis of the phenylpropanoid amino acids, L-phenylalanine and L-tyrosine, from carbohydrates

lignified walls. Most of the work on chemistry of lignin has been done with woods since it is simpler to make lignin preparations from them, but biosynthetic tracer studies have also used grasses and other herbaceous plants since they are simpler to grow and manipulate experimentally.

R–CH_2–CH(OH)–COOH ⇅ R–CH_2–CO–COOH ⇅ R–CH_2–CH(NH_2)–COOH

Shikimic Acid

R′–CH_2–CH(OH)–COOH ⇅ R′–CH_2–CO–COOH ⇅ R′–CH_2–CH(NH_2)–COOH

Phenylalanine Pool → Protein ← Tyrosine Pool

Fig. 5. Origin of phenylalanine and tyrosine in plants. R = phenyl; R′ = *p*-hydroxyphenyl

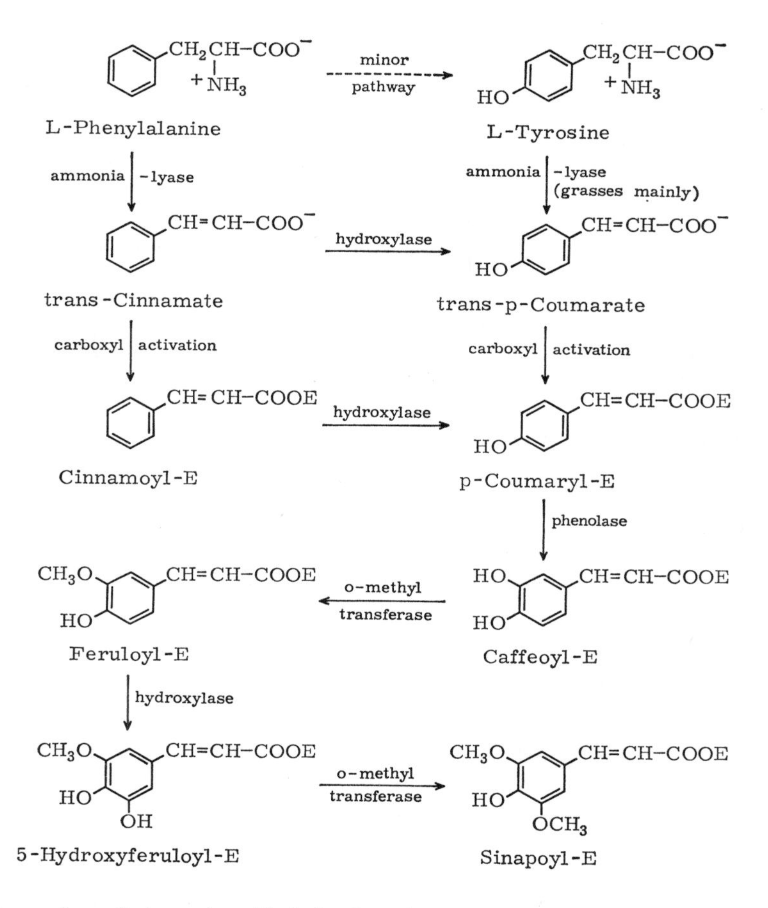

Fig. 6. Formation of cinnamic acid derivatives from the phenylpropanoid amino acids in plants. The intermediates are hydrolyzable substances soluble in water but not in ethanol or acetone (EL-BASYOUNI and NEISH, 1966). They are represented as esters of an unknown substance "E" in this figure. This unknown substance may be a protein

There has been enough work done to support the view that lignin is formed by the same general route in all vascular plants. The course followed is probably:

CO_2 → carbohydrates → phenylpropanoid amino acids → cinnamic acid derivatives → cinnamyl alcohol derivatives → lignin.

Like most plant constituents, lignin is probably formed from carbohydrates, which in turn are normally derived from the photosynthetic assimilation of carbon

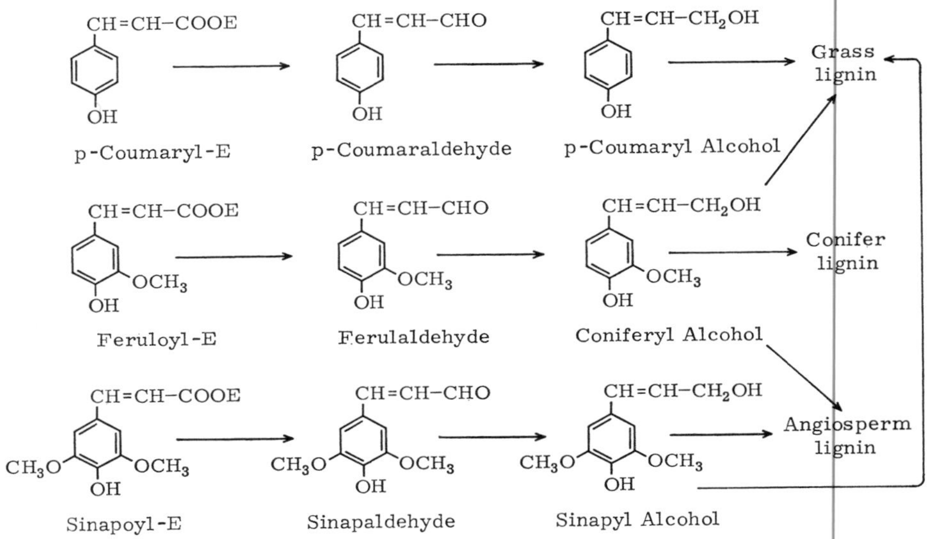

CH=CH–COOE → CH=CH–CHO → CH=CH–CH_2OH → Grass lignin

p-Coumaryl-E, p-Coumaraldehyde, p-Coumaryl Alcohol

CH=CH–COOE → CH=CH–CHO → CH=CH–CH_2OH → Conifer lignin

OCH_3, OH

Feruloyl-E, Ferulaldehyde, Coniferyl Alcohol

CH=CH–COOE → CH=CH–CHO → CH=CH–CH_2OH → Angiosperm lignin

CH_3O, OCH_3, OH

Sinapoyl-E, Sinapaldehyde, Sinapyl Alcohol

Fig. 7. Origin of lignins from cinnamic acid derivatives *via* the corresponding alcohols. This is an extension of Fig. 6. Small amounts of sinapyl alcohol and *p*-coumaryl alcohol are also incorporated into conifer lignin (Fr. pages 70 and 105)

dioxide. The first major step appears to be the formation of the phenylpropanoid amino acids (Figs. 4, 5). These can be converted to a number of cinnamic acid derivatives (Fig. 6), which upon reduction give corresponding cinnamyl alcohol derivatives (Fig. 7), from which lignin is formed by a "dehydropolymerization". A number of other phenolic compounds, which occur as secondary metabolites in plants, are biosynthetically related to lignin, as shown in Fig. 8. This chapter is concerned mainly with a discussion of the evidence for the metabolic pathways shown in these figures and, finally, some views on the phylogeny of lignin are expressed.

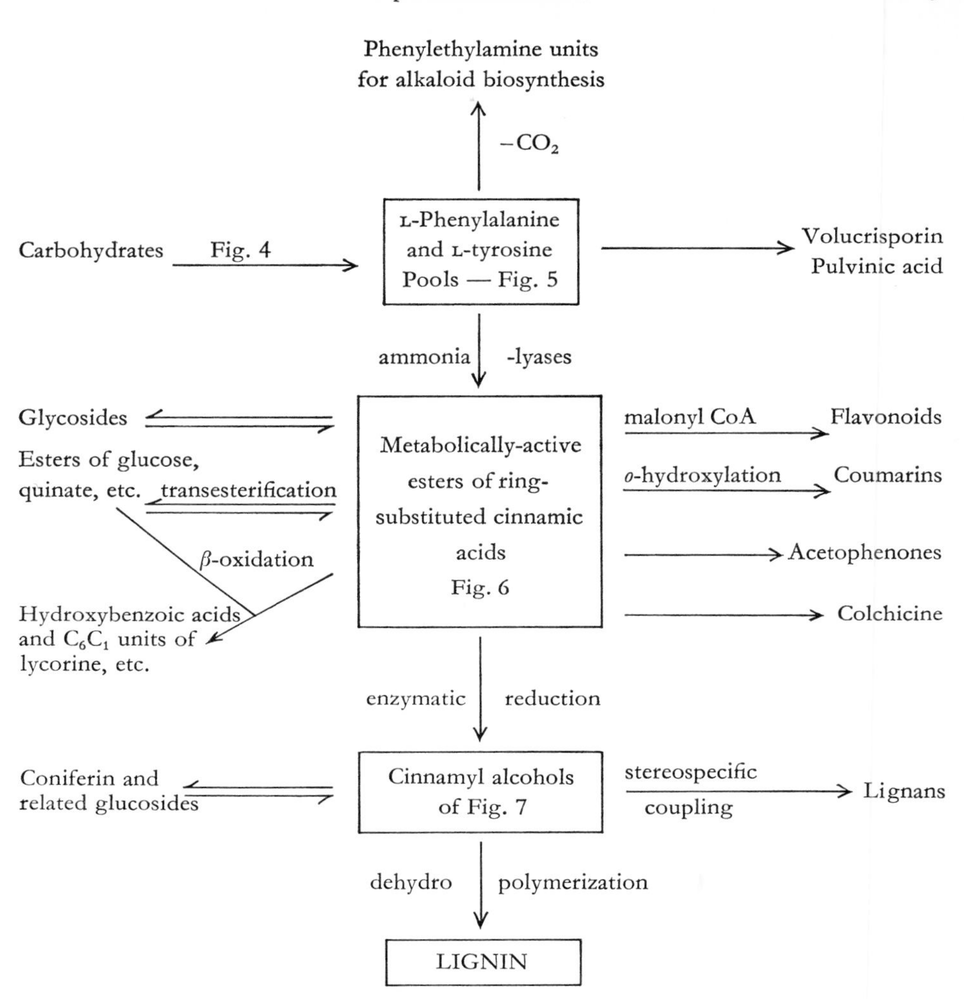

Fig. 8. Biogenetic relationship of lignin to other phenolic substances of plants

II. Experimental Methods

A. General Remarks

In working out biosynthetic pathways in plants both tracer and enzyme techniques have been used extensively. Use of the tracer method involves administering an isotopically-labelled compound (usually ^{14}C-labelled), which is suspected to be a precursor or intermediate, and then determining if it is incorporated appreciably into the end product and, if so, by what mechanism. This may mean using a precursor labelled in a known manner and determining the distribution of isotope in the product whose biosynthesis is being investigated. The results often suggest a possible pathway, which can be tested by feeding the hypothetical (labelled) intermediates. The plant material may also be investigated to see if enzymes catalyzing the postulated reactions can be demonstrated. Such investigations may reveal finer details concerning the actual reactions, or suggest modifications of the original scheme.

The degree of certainty in establishing a compound as an intermediate is quite variable, and it is useful to adopt the nomenclature proposed by DAVIS (1955). A *precursor* is thus defined as any compound which can be converted into the substance being studied, whether it is natural or not. A *natural intermediate* is a precursor which is known to be present in the organism being studied. An *obligate intermediate* is a compound which is an essential component of the biosynthetic pathway. Tracer and enzyme experiments have not done more than establish natural intermediates. There is always the possibility that an alternate, and perhaps more important, pathway exists. However, experiments with biochemical mutants of bacteria have established some obligate intermediates such as the shikimic acid in biosynthesis of the aromatic amino acids (Fig. 4).

B. Tracer Studies

1. *Feeding of Precursors*

Several methods of introducing labelled compounds into living plant material have been used in studies on lignin biosynthesis. Since the precursors tested are generally water-soluble, these methods have involved the introduction of aqueous solutions. The simplest method is the infusion technique, which is easily applied to fresh cuttings such as twigs of trees or shoots of herbaceous plants. The twig or shoot is cut from the plant (preferably under water), and the severed end is placed in an aqueous solution of the ^{14}C-labelled compound. The solution is absorbed into the cutting to make up losses due to transpiration of water. The initial volume of solution is made small enough so that it will practically all be absorbed in 1 to 2 h. The labelled solution is usually followed with several small portions of water, and in this way all of the precursor can be infused into the plant material. The cuttings are then transferred to water for the remainder of the metabolic period. Experiments of this type are usually run for 5 to 20 h. There is danger of the plant material becoming moribund if long periods are used.

The infusion method is not suitable where root tissues are required, or for long term experiments (REZNIK, 1960). In such experiments one may use root cultures, or tissue cultures. Alternatively the precursor may be introduced into the vascular system of an intact plant through a wound in the stem by injection or by a cotton wick, or fed in through the cut tips of branches or of leaves which are still attached to the plant.

Solid precursors have been introduced into spruce cambium by implantation under the bark (FREUDENBERG et al., 1955; KRATZL et al., 1957). Other examples used in studies on lignin formation include administering solutions through tips of spruce twigs after excision of needles (FREUDENBERG et al., 1955; ACERBO, SCHUBERT and NORD, 1960; SCHUBERT, 1962) and adding precursors to plant tissue cultures (HIGUCHI, 1962; BARNOUD et al., 1964). The infusion method has been most widely used in the studies reported in this chapter. It has also been applied successfully in studies on the synthesis of cell wall polysaccharides in wheat (NEISH, 1955; ALTERMATT and NEISH, 1956), rutin in buckwheat (UNDERHILL, WATKIN and NEISH, 1957), and pungenin in Colorado spruce (NEISH, 1959).

The infusion method is the simplest to apply to a variety of plants. The rapid, quantitative uptake of precursor minimizes the possibility of its destruction by microorganisms. Although this method is generally most suitable for experiments of approximately one day or less, this limitation is not a serious handicap. Quite often it is preferable to perform short-term experiments because there is less danger of randomization of labelling by recycling. For example, in a one-day experiment using the infusion technique WATKIN, UNDERHILL and NEISH (1957) showed that quercetin formed from acetate-^{14}C in buckwheat has 50 to 100 times as much ^{14}C in ring A as in ring B, whereas acetate fed through the roots during 6 days was found by GEISSMAN and SWAIN (1957) and SHIBATA and YAMAZAKI (1957) to give rise to quercetin with only 2 to 4 times as much ^{14}C in ring A as in ring B. Obviously the infusion technique has given a more clear-cut result.

A considerable saving of time and materials may be made by using the infusion technique as can be seen by comparing an experiment of KRATZL and FAIGLE (1959, 1960) with a similar experiment of ACERBO, SCHUBERT and NORD (1960). Both experiments were designed to determine the ^{14}C-distribution in the vanillin obtained from spruce lignin, after feeding D-glucose-1-^{14}C. Using the infusion technique, KRATZL and FAIGLE were able to obtain vanillin with 382 c.p.m./mg in 48 h from 0.1 mc of glucose. ACERBO, SCHUBERT and NORD administered ten times as much ^{14}C-labelled glucose to the upper branches of spruce trees through the cut ends of needles during 28 days and isolated vanillin with only 40 c.p.m./mg.

Other experiments from Kratzl's laboratory have shown that the method of feeding may influence the fate of the precursor. When KRATZL et al. (1957) administered ^{14}C-labelled coniferin to spruce branches by implantation of crystals under the bark, they found that the vanillin recovered by nitrobenzene oxidation of the wood residue was seven times as active as the vanilloyl methyl ketone obtained by ethanolysis. On the other hand, KRATZL and FAIGLE (1958) have shown that when labelled coniferin was fed by the infusion technique, subsequent degradation gave vanillin and vanilloyl methyl ketone with approximately equal specific activities. It is probable that the results were modified by a wound reaction when the implantation method was used. KRATZL (1965) has concluded that the infusion method is preferable.

There does not seem to be any universally superior method of administering labelled compounds to living plant material. All techniques except photosynthetic assimilation with $^{14}CO_2$ involve some departure from "normal" conditions. EL-BASYOUNI, NEISH and TOWERS (1964) have shown that $^{14}CO_2$ administered in this manner to wheat plants gives about the same distribution of isotope in the phenolic intermediates of lignin biosynthesis as does L-phenylalanine-G-^{14}C fed by the infusion method. The best method for any particular investigation is probably the simplest one which will give good incorporation of natural intermediates in a relatively short time without confusing the results by wound reactions or microbial decomposition. In studies where comparisons of the efficiency of incorporation are to be made, the amount of precursor fed per unit weight of plant material unit must be controlled (WATKIN and NEISH, 1960).

2. *Measurement of ^{14}C-Incorporation into Lignin*

Since lignin is difficult to obtain in a pure state, especially from herbaceous plants, most investigators have isolated simple compounds obtained by degradation of lignin *in situ*. The plant material is first ground and extracted to remove any unchanged precursors or soluble compounds formed from it. This extraction is often done by vigorous mechanical disintegration in hot 80% ethanol, followed by washing with hot absolute ethanol and other solvents such as ether and ethanol-benzene. This gives an "extractive-free" plant material which is a dry, finely-divided residue containing lignin and cell wall polysaccharides. When herbaceous plants are used, this fraction may contain a considerable amount (*ca.* 20%) of denatured protein as well. The extractive-free material is next subjected to one or more chemical procedures (Figs. 1, 2, 3) known to give simple compounds derived from lignin. These are purified and the ^{14}C-content is measured. In some experiments the distribution of ^{14}C in the molecule may be determined also.

Alkaline nitrobenzene oxidation (Fig. 1) of extractive-free plant material gives the best yield of aromatic compounds derived from lignin (FR. p. 61). FREUDENBERG, LAUTSCH and ENGLER (1940) found that spruce wood gave yields of vanillin up to 26% based on lignin. Angiospermous wood gave both vanillin and syringaldehyde (CREIGHTON, GIBBS and HIBBERT, 1944; TOWERS and GIBBS, 1953) in combined yields up to 45% of the lignin. Monocotyledons give *p*-hydroxybenzaldehyde in addition to vanillin and syringaldehyde. The tyrosine in protein may account for most of the *p*-hydroxybenzaldehyde obtained by oxidation of immature plant material (BROWN, WRIGHT and NEISH, 1959). KRATZL and his collaborators have developed a modification of this oxidation procedure which uses nitrobenzene-*m*-sulfonate in place of nitrobenzene (KRATZL et al., 1959). SMITH and NEISH (1964) have used alkaline copper oxidation to obtain ^{14}C-labelled vanillin from spruce lignin. The other carbons of the lignin phenylpropanoid units gave rise to carbon dioxide and formic acid.

Another useful oxidation method which has been applied to radiotracer experiments depends on prior methylation of the plant material (FREUDENBERG and NIEDERCORN, 1958). The procedure involves methylation with dimethyl sulfate and alkali, followed by alkaline hydrolysis to release phenol groups, then further methylation (FR. p. 100). The methylated wood meal is then oxidized by neutral permanganate to give hemipinic acid and related compounds (see Fig. 1).

Oxidative degradation does not give products with the phenylpropane skeleton, since it removes two carbons of the side chain, but certain non-oxidative degradation procedures do give simple phenylpropane derivatives. For example, HIBBERT and co-workers (HIBBERT, 1942; CRAMER, HUNTER and HIBBERT, 1939) obtained a mixture of water-soluble phenylpropanoid ketones by ethanolysis of wood meals (see Fig. 2). These compounds, now known as "Hibbert's ketones", were obtained only as guaiacyl derivatives from coniferous woods whereas both guaiacyl and syringyl derivatives were isolated following ethanolysis of angiospermous woods. KRATZL and co-workers have used ethanolysis extensively in tracer experiments on the biosynthesis of spruce lignin (KRATZL et al., 1959; KRATZL, 1961; KRATZL, 1965). Fig. 2 is a brief outline of the procedure as used by KRATZL et al. (1959). Recently KRATZL and CZEPEL (1964) have used gas chromatography to fractionate ethanolysis products obtained from spruce.

BREWER, COOKE and HIBBERT (1948) found that hydrogenolysis of angiosperm wood in aqueous dioxane containing a small amount of HCl gave dihydroconiferyl and dihydrosinapyl alcohols (Fig. 3). This procedure was adapted to radiotracer experiments by BROWN and NEISH (1959). These phenylpropanoid alcohols are closely related to the monomers from which lignin is believed to be formed. Fig. 3 also outlines another procedure which has been used in radiotracer experiments by the Vienna school (KRATZL, 1961; KRATZL, 1965; KRATZL et al., 1959) on sulfonic acids from spruce lignin. Their studies indicate that the vanillin and acetaldehyde, obtained by alkaline hydrolysis of sulfonated lignin, together include all the carbons of a phenylpropane unit.

Each of these methods of degradation has given results of value, and each has its advantages and disadvantages. The nitrobenzene oxidation gives a relatively high yield of aldehydes, which are readily purified. This makes it the method of choice when a wide range of precursors is to be tested over a number of plant species, especially when these include a number of herbaceous species having a relatively low lignin content. The chief disadvantage of this method is that a phenylpropanoid compound is not isolated, and there is always the possibility that the aldehydes are originating from an artifact that is not a phenylpropanoid polymer. Application of the more difficult techniques of ethanolysis or hydrogenolysis will tell whether the insoluble substance formed from the labelled precursor is phenylpropanoid or not. This confirmation is desirable for compounds which have been shown to be effective "lignin precursors" by the nitrobenzene oxidation technique.

There are several methods in use for expressing the efficiency of ^{14}C incorporation into lignin. The dilution value is useful since it does not require a knowledge of the lignin content. This value is calculated by dividing the specific activity of the labelled precursor by the specific activity of the purified degradation product. This ratio is an indication of the extent to which the isotope has been diluted in the plant and is related to the efficiency of incorporation, since when there is only a small incorporation there is a large dilution by the unlabelled lignin pre-existing in the plant. If the lignin content at the end of the experiment is known, the total ^{14}C incorporated into lignin can be calculated and from this the "per cent conversion" of the precursor. If comparisons of the efficiency of incorporation are to be made, the weight of precursor fed per unit weight of plant material (i.e. the dosage) should be constant. Dilution values are especially sensitive to variation in dosage (WATKIN and NEISH, 1960).

C. Enzyme Studies

The first clear recognition of an enzyme was the separation of a crude amylase (diastase) from malt extract by PAYEN and PERSOZ (1833). Although this work got plant enzymology off to an early start, since then enzyme studies on plants have fallen far behind similar work with other organisms. Most purification procedures have been developed for enzymes from animal tissues or from microorganisms, primarily yeast and bacteria (DIXON and WEBB, 1964).

Workers interested in plant enzymes have applied the general methods of enzymology to their problems. In the later stages of a purification, when one is dealing mainly with a mixture of soluble proteins, these methods would be expected to work as well as with proteins from another source. However, in the early stages there are some problems peculiar to plants. Vascular plants contain, in addition to lignin, other phenolic substances (tannins, phenolic acid esters, flavonoid compounds, coumarins, etc.) which are not usually found in animal tissues or in microorganisms. When the plant material is ground in a buffer, the hydrolases and phenoloxidases released can catalyze reactions with these phenolic substrates which might result in rapid inactivation of many other enzymes. It is perhaps significant that most successful plant enzyme work has been based on bland plant materials such as spinach or leguminous seedlings which are not especially rich in phenolic compounds.

It is not possible to suggest any general procedure for demonstrating or isolating enzymes involved in lignification. Some of these enzymes may have a rather broad substrate specificity and may even occur in organisms which are not lignified. In attempts to demonstrate enzymes associated with the metabolism of aromatic compounds in vascular plants, however, several courses are open. One approach is to use plant materials from which experience has shown that other enzymes can be easily extracted. Inhibitors of destructive enzymes may be added to the extraction medium. For example, JONES, HULME and WOOLTORTON (1965) found polyvinylpyrrolidine to be useful in the extraction of enzymes from apples, because it combines with phenolase and thus avoids the inhibition of enzymes by oxidation products of phenols. Another useful approach involves separating the phenols from the enzymes. Some success can be expected here by preparation of an acetone powder. The cold acetone dissolves many of the phenols and separates them from the plant proteins before appreciable enzyme action can occur. Some phenols remain in the acetone-insoluble fraction. Presumably these are chemically bound to the polysaccharides and proteins. However, preparation of an acetone powder has been advantageous in some instances, e.g. in the demonstration of L-tyrosine ammonia-lyase in barley shoots (NEISH, 1961). The presence of this enzyme could be easily demonstrated in acetone-dried material but it was difficult to detect in fresh frozen shoots ground in buffer.

BARLEY shoots (about 20 g) are cut into lengths 2 to 4 cm long and covered with acetone chilled to —20°, in a Waring blendor. The mixture is blended for approximately 1 min, filtered rapidly by suction and washed with chilled acetone. The fibrous residue is air-dried on the filter and then in an air stream at room temperature. Finally it is dried *in vacuo* for about 1 h. An aliquot of this acetone dried plant material (0.2 g) is mixed intimately in a culture tube with 3 ml of tris hydroxymethyl aminomethane buffer (pH 8.8, 0.05 M) containing 0.1% of L-tyrosine. A second mixture, without tyrosine, is also prepared and both tubes are incubated 3 h at room temperature. The contents are then diluted by 7 ml of water and filtered. The filtrate is acidified by 5 N HCl (0.2 ml) and extracted once with 10 ml of ether. The ether is evaporated at room temperature and the residue dissolved in 0.2 ml of 95% ethanol. The presence of p-coumaric acid in this solution is easily demonstrated by paper chromatography (IBRAHIM and TOWERS, 1960) using benzene-acetic acid-water as the irrigant. This acid is easily recognized as a fluorescent spot under ultraviolet light which is visible immediately after the paper has been exposed to ammonia vapor, but not before. The sample incubated with tyrosine shows a strong spot for p-coumaric acid which is weak or absent when tyrosine is omitted. p-Coumaric acid can be demonstrated in a more sophisticated manner if ^{14}C-labelled tyrosine is used and the chromatogram is scanned by a strip counter.

Assays for L-tyrosine ammonia-lyase or L-phenylalanine ammonia-lyase have been based on quantitative measurement of ^{14}C in the ether-soluble acids obtained by incubation with ^{14}C-labelled tyrosine or phenylalanine, respectively (KOUKOL and CONN, 1961; NEISH, 1961; YOUNG, TOWERS and NEISH, 1966).

III. Biosynthesis of Aromatic Amino Acids in Plants

A. Summary of Work with Bacterial Mutants

The aromatic amino acids, L-phenylalanine, L-tyrosine and L-tryptophan, occur ubiquitously. These compounds can be synthesized from carbohydrates by plants and many microorganisms, but not by animals. The intermediates involved in the conversion of carbohydrates to phenylalanine and tyrosine by heterotrophic bacteria are well known, and are shown in Fig. 4. This scheme is based on studies of nutritional mutants of *Escherichia coli* and *Aerobacter aerogenes*.

These studies involved isolation of mutants unable to convert carbohydrates to the aromatic amino acids, and an investigation of their nutritional requirements. This work has been reviewed by DAVIS (1955, 1958) and by SPRINSON (1960). The key to this scheme was the discovery (see DAVIS, 1955) that a requirement of a mutant strain of *E. coli* for five aromatic compounds (phenylalanine, tyrosine, tryptophan, *p*-aminobenzoic acid and *p*-hydroxybenzoic acid) could be satisfied completely by a single compound, shikimic acid, thus establishing this acid as an *obligate intermediate* in the biosynthesis of aromatic rings in *E. coli*. Further nutritional studies involving other mutant strains, and enzyme and tracer techniques, have resulted in the scheme summarized in Fig. 4. The last intermediate to be identified was chorismic acid which was found by GIBSON and co-workers to be accumulated by an auxotroph of *A. aerogenes* (GIBSON and JACKMAN, 1963; GIBSON and GIBSON, 1964; GIBSON, 1964). Chorismic acid is the last intermediate common to the biosynthesis of all essential aromatic compounds in these bacteria. It is at this point that paths diverge which lead to prephenic acid, anthranilic acid (and later tryptophan), *p*-hydroxybenzoic acid and probably *p*-aminobenzoic acid. We are concerned here only with the prephenic acid pathway which leads to L-phenylalanine and L-tyrosine, and with the question of its occurrence in vascular plants.

B. Studies on Vascular Plants

It is likely that phenylalanine and tyrosine are synthesized in plants by the same route as in bacteria. Since it is impractical to work with nutritional mutants of vascular plants, this can not be demonstrated with the same elegance as was possible with bacteria. All the tracer and enzyme studies, with higher plants reported so far however lend support to the scheme outlined in Fig. 4. This work has been reviewed previously [NEISH, 1964 (1); CONN, 1964].

Shikimic acid is known to occur widely in plants (HASEGAWA, 1962). Shikimic acid labelled with ^{14}C was incorporated into both phenylalanine and tyrosine by *Salvia splendens* (scarlet sage) [MCCALLA and NEISH, 1959 (1, 2)], *Triticum aestivum* (wheat) and *Fagopyrum tataricum* (buckwheat) (GAMBORG and NEISH, 1959). Since these plants belong to three different families, it is probable that vascular plants in general can use shikimic acid for formation of aromatic amino acids. Quinic acid also occurs widely in higher plants, and there is evidence that it may be more important in the biosynthesis of phenylalanine and tyrosine than it is in bacteria. Using young rose plants, WEINSTEIN, PORTER and LAURENCOT [1959 (2)] prepared ^{14}C-labelled quinic acid from $^{14}CO_2$. The quinic acid isolated had a higher specific activity than shikimic acid from the same source. When quinate-^{14}C was fed to roses, it was converted to shikimic acid, phenylalanine and tyrosine. This observation was extended to nine species of vascular plants [WEINSTEIN, LAURENCOT and PORTER, 1959 (1), 1961, 1962]. GOLDSCHMID and QUIMBY (1964) have shown that quinic acid and shikimic acid can be interconverted in twigs of *Tsuga heterophylla*, but the kinetics of the process did not indicate a direct precursor-product relationship.

Tracer studies by GAMBORG and NEISH (1959) showed ready interconversion of phenylpropanoid α-hydroxy, α-oxo and α-amino acids in both *Triticum aestivum* and *Fagopyrum tataricum* with different pools for the phenyl and *p*-hydroxyphenyl derivatives. These are called the phenylalanine and tyrosine pools, respectively (see Fig. 5). When one of the compounds in these pools was administered, it was readily converted to the corresponding amino acid, both free and bound in protein. Compounds of the tyrosine pool did not form phenylalanine but there was a slight conversion to tyrosine of the compounds comprising the phenylalanine pool. However, shikimic acid was a better precursor of tyrosine than any compound in the phenylalanine pool. This suggests that plants are like bacteria in forming tyrosine from prephenic acid, as shown in Fig. 4, but they have an alternate pathway, also known to exist in animals, i.e. the hydroxylation of phenylalanine. It is not known if the hydroxy acids of Fig. 5 have any physiological significance in plants. GAMBORG, WETTER and NEISH (1962) have shown that cell-free preparations from wheat shoots will readily oxidize the α-hydroxy acids to the α-oxo acids, but this activity paralleled the activity of glycolic acid oxidase during a twenty-fold purification. Thus the incorporation of ^{14}C from the hydroxy acids of Fig. 5 into the corresponding amino acids may be a side reaction due to a lack of specificity of oxidase systems, which have a primary metabolic role not directly related to synthesis of the phenylpropanoid amino acids.

Plants are known to contain enzymes which catalyze some of the reactions of Fig. 4. CONN (1964) has reviewed work on the properties of these enzymes. The enzyme 5-dehydroquinate hydro-lyase (E.C. 4.2.1.10), which catalyzes reaction 2 of Fig. 4, was detected in peas and spinach by MITSUHASHI and DAVIS (1954) and purified from cauliflower buds by BALINSKY and DAVIES [1961 (3)]. Shikimate: NADP oxidoreductase (E.C. 1.1.1.25), which catalyzes reaction 3, was found in pea seedlings by BALINSKY and DAVIES [1961 (1, 2)] and in mung bean seedlings by NANDY and GANGULI [1961 (1)]. This enzyme does not act on quinic or dehydroquinic acid and hence does not catalyze reaction 1. NANDY and GANGULI [1961 (2)] also obtained a cell-free extract of mung beans that would convert glucose 6-phosphate to dehydroshikimic acid. Microsomes and supernatant fluid were both essential, but the supernatant alone could catalyze conversion of a mixture of phosphoenolpyruvate and erythrose 4-phosphate to dehydroshikimic acid. This indicates a close analogy between synthesis of shikimic acid in higher plants and microorganisms. Reaction 1 of Fig. 4 is catalyzed by quinate: NAD oxidoreductase (E.C. 1.1.1.24), an enzyme which is found in certain bacteria but has not yet been reported in higher plants. The actual mechanism for conversion of quinate to shikimate in plants has not been established, and may differ from that shown in Fig. 4.

Intermediates between shikimic acid and prephenic acid and enzymes acting on them have not yet been found in vascular plants. However, the formation of phenylalanine by a transamination between phenylpyruvate and glutamic acid has been demonstrated by KRETOVICH and USPENSKAYA (1958) in homogenates of pea seedlings. GAMBORG and WETTER (1963) purified a transaminase from mung beans which catalyzed transamination of phenylalanine or tyrosine in the presence of pyruvate or α-oxoglutarate. As previously mentioned, both shikimic and quinic acid occur widely in the plant kingdom. They are probably formed from carbohydrates and converted to the aromatic amino acids as shown in Fig. 4, but alternate pathways may exist.

IV. Ring-substituted Cinnamic Acids as Intermediates in Lignification

A. General Remarks

There is good evidence from radiotracer and enzyme studies that cinnamic acid derivatives are formed from phenylalanine and tyrosine, as shown in Fig. 6. This work has been reviewed recently by BROWN (1964), CONN (1964), NEISH [1964 (1, 2)] and by HIGUCHI, BARNOUD and ROBERT (1964). The ring-substituted cinnamic acids of Fig. 6 are widely distributed in vascular plants (BATE-SMITH, 1956, 1962) particularly *p*-coumaric and ferulic acids. They occur as esters rather than as free acids, however, and it is uncertain which esters may actually be involved as intermediates in lignification. Recent work by EL-BASYOUNI, NEISH and TOWERS (1964) has shown that numerous esters are present in the wheat plant, some being soluble in ethanol and others insoluble. It was found, unexpectedly, that esters acting as intermediates on the direct path to lignin were insoluble in ethanol.

B. Tracer Studies

1. Comparison of Precursors

Tracer experiments with ^{14}C-labelled precursors have led to the hypothesis that aromatic amino acids, especially phenylalanine, contribute the carbon from which lignin is synthesized and that certain derivatives of cinnamic acid function as intermediates. Experiments have been conducted in which ^{14}C-labelled compounds have been administered to plants and the efficiency of their incorporation into lignin measured (see Table 1). In some instances the distribution of ^{14}C has been determined

Table 1. *Effectiveness of various ^{14}C-labelled compounds as precursors of lignin in vivo*

Compound fed	Substances isolated	Species	Reference
		A. Degree of Incorporation — Good	
Shikimic acid-G-^{14}C	Vanillin and syringaldehyde	Triticum aestivum[a] Acer Negundo	Brown and Neish [1955 (1)]
	Hibbert's ketones Vanillin	Pinus strobus (tissue cultures)	Hasegawa, Higuchi and Ishikawa (1960)
Shikimic acid-2,6-^{14}C	Vanillin	Saccharum officinarum	Eberhardt and Schubert (1956)
L-Phenylalanine-G-^{14}C	Vanillin and syringaldehyde	Triticum aestivum Acer Negundo Populus balsamifera	Brown and Neish [1955 (1), 1955 (2), 1956, 1959]
		Caragana arborescens Sparganium multipedunculatum	Wright, Brown and Neish (1958)
		Triglochin maritima Alisma triviale Hordeum vulgare Bromus inermis Scirpus validus Juncus bufonius Juncus nodosus Zinnia elegans Lepachys columniferae Carex laeviconica Calamagrostis inexpansa Smilacina stellata Salix amygdaloides Melilotus officinalis Eleagnus commutata Fagopyrum tataricum	Brown (1961)

Table 1. Part A. (Continued)

Compound fed	Substances isolated	Species	Reference
L-Phenylalanine-G-^{14}C	Vanillin and syringaldehyde	Eucalyptus sideroxylon E. camaldulensis Ginkgo biloba	Bland (1963)
		Ulmus campestris and tissue cultures of Sequoia sempervirens Syringa vulgaris Rosa wichuraiana Daucus carota	Barnoud et al. (1964)
	Vanillin	Avena sativa Hordeum vulgare Secale cereale Lolium multiflorum L. perenne L. temulentum Bromus arvensis Poa trivialis Dactylis glomerata Lupinus luteus	Schütte and Freyer (1965)
	Hibbert's ketones	Pinus strobus (tissue cultures) Triticum aestivum	Higuchi (1962) Higuchi and Brown [1963 (1)]
	Dihydroconiferyl and dihydrosinapyl alcohols	Triticum aestivum Acer Negundo	Brown and Neish (1959)
DL-Phenylalanine-α-^{14}C[f]	Isohemipinic acid	Picea excelsa	Freudenberg and Niedercorn (1958)
	Active lignin Hemipinic acids	Picea excelsa	Freudenberg and Lehman (1963)

Table 1. Part A. (Continued)

Compound fed	Substances isolated	Species	Reference
DL-Phenylalanine-β-^{14}C[t]	Vanillin and syringaldehyde	Eucalyptus sideroxylon	BLAND (1963)
	Vanillin	Picea pungens P. ajanensis	SCHÜTTE and FREYER (1965)
L-Tyrosine-G-^{14}C	Vanillin and syringaldehyde	Triticum aestivum Hordeum vulgare Bromus inermis Calamagrostis inexpansa Eucalyptus sideroxylon	BROWN and NEISH (1956); BROWN (1961) BLAND (1963)
L-Phenyllactic acid-β-^{14}C[t]	Vanillin and syringaldehyde	Triticum aestivum Acer Negundo Fagopyrum tataricum Carex atherodes Salvia splendens	WRIGHT, BROWN and NEISH (1958)
D-Phenyllactic acid-β-^{14}C[t]	Vanillin and syringaldehyde	Triticum aestivum Flaminia festucacea Carex atherodes	WRIGHT, BROWN and NEISH (1958)
DL-*p*-Hydroxyphenyllactic acid-β-^{14}C[t]	Vanillin and syringaldehyde	Triticum aestivum	BROWN, WRIGHT and NEISH (1959)
Phenylpyruvic acid-β-^{14}C[t]	Vanillin and syringaldehyde	Triticum aestivum	BROWN and NEISH [1955 (2)]
p-Hydroxyphenylpyruvic acid (carboxyl-labelled)	Klason lignin	Saccharum officinarum	ACERBO, SCHUBERT and NORD (1958)
p-Hydroxyphenylpyruvic acid-β-^{14}C[t]	Vanillin and syringaldehyde	Triticum aestivum	BROWN, WRIGHT and NEISH (1959)
Dihydrocinnamic acid-β-^{14}C[t]	Vanillin and syringaldehyde	Triticum aestivum	BROWN and NEISH (1956)

Table 1. Part A. (Continued)

Compound fed	Substances isolated	Species	Reference
Cinnamic acid-β-$^{14}C^{t}$	Vanillin and syringaldehyde	Triticum aestivum Acer Negundo	BROWN and NEISH [1955 (2), 1956]
Cinnamic acid-ring, β-$^{14}C^{t}$	Vanillin and syringaldehyde	Picea mariana Populus tremuloides	SMITH and NEISH (1964)
Cinnamic acid-α-$^{14}C^{t}$	Dihydroconiferyl and dihydrosinapyl alcohols	Triticum aestivum Acer Negundo	BROWN and NEISH (1959)
Cinnamic acid-α-$^{14}C^{t}$	Klason lignin	Picea mariana Populus tremuloides	SMITH and NEISH (1964)
Cinnamic acid (carboxyl-labelled)	Klason lignin	Picea mariana Populus tremuloides	SMITH and NEISH (1964)
p-Coumaric acid-β-$^{14}C^{t}$	Vanillin and syringaldehyde	Triticum aestivum Acer Negundo	BROWN and NEISH (1956)
p-Coumaric acid-α-$^{14}C^{t}$	Hibbert's ketones	Pinus strobus (tissue cultures) Triticum aestivum	HIGUCHI (1962) HIGUCHI and BROWN [1963 (1)]
Caffeic acid-β-$^{14}C^{t}$	Vanillin and syringaldehyde	Triticum aestivum Acer Negundo	BROWN and NEISH (1956)
Ferulic acid-β-$^{14}C^{t}$	Vanillin and syringaldehyde	Triticum aestivum Acer Negundo	BROWN and NEISH [1955 (2), 1956]
	Dihydroconiferyl and dihydrosinapyl alcohols	Triticum aestivum	BROWN and NEISH (1959)
Ferulic acid-α-$^{14}C^{t}$	Hibbert's ketones	Pinus strobus (tissue cultures) Triticum aestivum	HIGUCHI (1962) HIGUCHI and BROWN [1963 (1)]

Table 1. Part A. (Continued)

Compound fed	Substances isolated	Species	Reference
Sinapic acid-β-^{14}C[f]	Vanillin and syringaldehyde[b]	Triticum aestivum Acer Negundo	BROWN and NEISH (1956)
Sinapic acid-α-^{14}C[f]	Hibbert's ketones	Triticum aestivum	HIGUCHI and BROWN [1963 (1)]
Coniferin-(carbinol-^{14}C)	Histochemical radioautography	Picea excelsa	FREUDENBERG et al. (1955)
Coniferin-2-^{14}C	Vanillin and acetaldehyde[c]	Picea excelsa	KRATZL and HOFBAUER (1958)
Coniferin-3-^{14}C	Vanillin and acetaldehyde[d]	Picea excelsa	KRATZL and HOFBAUER (1958)
	Hibbert's ketones[e] Vanillin	Picea excelsa	KRATZL and BILLEK (1959)
	Hibbert's ketones	Picea excelsa	KRATZL et al. (1957, 1959)
Vanillin-(carbonyl-^{14}C) D-glucoside	Histochemical radioautography	Picea excelsa	FREUDENBERG et al. (1955)
B. Degree of Incorporation — Fair			
Protocatechuic acid (carboxyl-labelled)	Vanillin and syringaldehyde	Populus balsamifera	BROWN and NEISH [1955 (2)]
p-Hydroxybenzoic acid (carboxyl-labelled)	Vanillin and syringaldehyde	Triticum aestivum	BROWN and NEISH [1955 (2)]
Syringic acid (carboxyl-labelled)	Vanillin and syringaldehyde	Triticum aestivum	BROWN and NEISH [1955 (2)]
Vanillin (carbonyl-labelled)	Vanillin and syringaldehyde	Triticum aestivum	BROWN and NEISH [1955 (2)]
	Hibbert's ketones	Picea excelsa	KRATZL et al. (1957)

Table 1. Part B. (Continued)

Compound fed	Substances isolated	Species	Reference
Vanillyl alcohol (carbinol-^{14}C)	Hibbert's ketones	Picea excelsa	Kratzl et al. (1957)
Vanillic acid (carboxyl-labelled)	Vanillin and syringaldehyde	Triticum aestivum	Brown and Neish [1955 (2)]
	Hibbert's ketones	Picea excelsa	Kratzl et al. (1957)
DL-Phenylhydracrylic acid-β-^{14}C[f]	Vanillin and syringaldehyde	Triticum aestivum	Wright, Brown and Neish (1958)
D-Phenyllactic acid-β-^{14}C[f]	Vanillin and syringaldehyde	Salvia splendens	Wright, Brown and Neish (1958)
3-Methoxy-4-hydroxytoluene-7-^{14}C	Hibbert's ketones Vanillin	Picea excelsa	Kratzl et al. (1959)
L-Tyrosine (generally labelled)	Vanillin and syringaldehyde	Zinnia elegans	Brown (1961)
L-Tyrosine-G-^{14}C	Vanillin	Picea pungens P. ajanensis	Schütte and Freyer (1965)
Sinapic acid-α-^{14}C[f]	Hibbert's ketones Ethanol lignin	Pinus strobus (tissue cultures)	Higuchi (1962)
5-Hydroxyferulic acid-α-^{14}C[f]	Syringoyl methyl ketone	Triticum aestivum	Higuchi and Brown [1963 (2)]
	C. Degree of Incorporation — Poor		
Acetate-2-^{14}C	Vanillin and syringaldehyde	Triticum aestivum Acer Negundo	Brown and Neish (1959)
	Dihydroconiferyl alcohol	Triticum aestivum Acer Negundo	Brown and Neish (1959)
	Hibbert's ketones	Eucalyptus nitens	Hasegawa and Higuchi (1960)

Table 1. Part C. (Continued)

Compound fed	Substances isolated	Species	Reference
	Vanillin and syringaldehyde	Pinus strobus (tissue culture)	Hasegawa, Higuchi and Ishikawa (1960)
Acetate-1-^{14}C	Vanillin	Picea excelsa	Kratzl and Faigle (1959, 1960)
	Vanillin and syringaldehyde	Eucalyptus sideroxylon	Bland (1963)
Benzoic acid (carboxyl-labelled)	Vanillin and syringaldehyde	Triticum aestivum	Brown and Neish [1955 (2)]
p-Anisic acid (carboxyl-labelled)	Vanillin and syringaldehyde	Triticum aestivum	Brown and Neish [1955 (2)]
	Dihydroconiferyl and dihydrosinapyl alcohol	Acer Negundo	Brown and Neish (1959)
Protocatechuic acid (carboxyl-labelled)	Vanillin and syringaldehyde	Triticum aestivum Acer Negundo	Brown and Neish [1955 (1), 1955 (2)]
Trimethylgallic acid (carboxyl-labelled)	Vanillin and syringaldehyde	Triticum aestivum	Brown and Neish [1955 (2)]
p-Hydroxybenzaldehyde (Carbonyl-labelled)	Vanillin and syringaldehyde	Triticum aestivum	Wright, Brown and Neish (1958)
	Hibbert's ketones Vanillin	Picea excelsa	Kratzl and Billek (1959)
Vanillin (carbonyl-labelled)	Dihydroconiferyl and dihydrosinapyl alcohols	Acer Negundo	Brown and Neish (1959)
Vanillin-carbonyl-^{14}C-L-glucoside	No fixation	Picea excelsa	Freudenberg et al. (1955)

Table 1. Part C. (Continued)

Compound fed	Substances isolated	Species	Reference
Homoveratrol (C-methyl labelled) Veratryl alcohol (carbinol-labelled) Veratryl aldehyde (carbonyl-labelled) Veratric acid (carboxyl-labelled)	Extractive-free residue	Picea excelsa	KRATZL et al. (1959)
DL-Mandelic acid-2-^{14}C	Vanillin and syringaldehyde	Triticum aestivum	WRIGHT, BROWN and NEISH (1958)
L-Tyrosine-G-^{14}C	Vanillin and syringaldehyde	Acer Negundo Populus balsamifera Caragana arborescens	BROWN and NEISH [1955 (2)]
		Carex laeviconica Calamagrostis inexpansa Smilacina stellata Salix amygdaloides Melilotus officinalis Eleagnus commutata Fagopyrum tataricum	BROWN and NEISH (1956)
		Sparganium multipedunculatum Triglochin maritima Alisma triviale Scirpus validus Juncus bufonius Juncus nodosus Populus balsamifera Lepachys columnifera	BROWN (1961)
		Eucalyptus camaldulensis	BLAND (1963)
	Vanillin	Lupinus luteus	SCHÜTTE and FREYER (1965)
DL-*threo*-Phenylglyceric acid-β-^{14}C[f]	Vanillin and syringaldehyde	Triticum aestivum	WRIGHT, BROWN and NEISH (1958)

Table 1. Part C. (Continued)

Compound fed	Substances isolated	Species	Reference
DL-*erythro*-Phenylglyceric acid-β-^{14}C[f]	Vanillin and syringaldehyde	Triticum aestivum	Wright, Brown and Neish (1958)
D-Phenyliactic acid-β-^{14}C[f]	Vanillin and syringaldehyde	Fagopyrum tataricum	Wright, Brown and Neish (1958)
p-Hydroxyphenylpyruvic acid-β-^{14}C[f]	Vanillin and syringaldehyde	Fagopyrum tataricum Salvia splendens	Brown, Wright and Neish (1959)
	Acid lignin Hibbert's ketones Vanillin	Picea excelsa	Kratzl and Billek (1959)
DL-*p*-Hydroxyphenyllactic acid -β-^{14}C[f]	Vanillin and syringaldehyde	Fagopyrum tataricum	Brown, Wright and Neish (1959)
m-Methoxycinnamic acid-β-^{14}C[f]	Vanillin and syringaldehyde	Triticum aestivum Acer Negundo	Brown and Neish (1956)
Sinapic acid-β-^{14}C[f]	Dihydroconiferyl and dihydrosinapyl alcohols	Acer Negundo	Brown and Neish (1959)
Coniferin-(carbinol-^{14}C)-(L-glucoside)	No fixation	Picea excelsa	Freudenberg et al. (1955)
Acetaminocinnamic acid-β-^{14}C[f]	Vanillin and syringaldehyde	Triticum aestivum	Brown and Neish [1955 (2)]

[a] Referred to as *Triticum vulgare* in some papers.
[b] Incorporation good in syringaldehyde, fair in vanillin.
[c] Incorporated into the acetaldehyde formed by alkaline hydrolysis of lignin sulfonic acids.
[d] Incorporated into the vanillin formed by hydrolysis of lignin sulfonic acids.
[e] Isolated as Ni salt of dioxime of vanilloyl methyl ketone.
[f] In the phenylpropanoid acids α refers to the carbon next to the carboxyl group and β refers to the ring-adjacent carbon.

to see whether or not randomization has occurred in the plant. Simple compounds such as carbon dioxide and carbohydrates have been used; but these are not included in Table 1 because it is known that these compounds are the precursors of all carbon compounds in plants. Experiments by STONE (1953) with $^{14}CO_2$ have shown that lignin was labelled readily by photosynthetic assimilation and that during subsequent metabolism in an ordinary atmosphere the ^{14}C incorporated in the lignin remained there. The incorporation of glucose into lignin has been demonstrated by HASEGAWA and HIGUCHI (1960); KRATZL and FAIGLE (1959, 1960); ACERBO, SCHUBERT and NORD (1960) and BLAND (1963). KRATZL and ZAUNER (1962) have also demonstrated the incorporation of ^{14}C from uniformly-labelled xylitol into spruce lignin, and interpreted this as being due to the operation of the pentose phosphate pathway to give hexose phosphates. COSCIA et al. (1962) have shown that generally-labelled sodium pyruvate was incorporated into birch lignin but not as an intact unit. Since the pyruvate carbon was found mainly in the terminal carbon of a C_6C_3 unit, they interpreted their results as showing operation of the "carboxylate shuttle" in plants.

There are two main pathways for formation of aromatic rings in plants, one by way of the shikimic acid pathway and the other by the acetate pathway [NEISH, 1964 (2)]. It appears from the results in Table 1 that the acetate pathway is not important in lignin formation, but rather that lignin is derived from carbohydrate *via* shikimic acid. The precursors listed in Table 1 are grouped as being "good", "fair" or "poor" and, in general, these groupings differ by an order of magnitude with reference to degree of incorporation. However, the arrangement is somewhat arbitrary because, unless compounds are compared in the same experiment at equivalent dosages, it is difficult to rate them accurately for their relative efficiency. Shikimic acid has been shown by several workers to be a good precursor, whereas acetate has been found to be a poor precursor by everyone who has tried it. Shikimic acid is probably incorporated into lignin by way of the amino acid, phenylalanine and in some instances tyrosine as well.

EBERHARDT and SCHUBERT (1956) showed that shikimic acid was converted to the aromatic guaiacyl group of lignin without randomization of the ring carbons. KRATZL and FAIGLE (1959, 1960) as well as ACERBO, SCHUBERT and NORD (1960) found that glucose-1-^{14}C also gave guaiacyl nuclei of lignin with the labelling pattern which would be expected if formed by the sequence of reactions: glucose → shikimic acid → guaiacyl nuclei of lignin. Probably all this work on the incorporation of shikimic acid into lignin is merely an indirect way of showing that plants can convert shikimic acid to phenylalanine. It is now well established, from work to be reviewed, that phenylalanine is a good precursor of lignin in all species tested, and it has been shown above that shikimic acid is an intermediate in the biosynthesis of phenylalanine in plants.

BROWN and NEISH (1956) and BROWN (1961) have shown that phenylalanine can be incorporated into lignin (vanillin and syringaldehyde) by a number of species of angiosperms. FREUDENBERG and NIEDERCORN (1958) have shown that phenylalanine can act as a precursor of spruce lignin (isohemipinic acid), and HIGUCHI (1962) has observed its incorporation into lignin (Hibbert's ketones) by tissue cultures of *Pinus strobus*. BROWN and NEISH (1959) have demonstrated that phenylalanine-^{14}C also labels lignin in wheat and maple, as measured by isolation of dihydroconiferyl alcohol and dihydrosinapyl alcohol following hydrogenolysis. BLAND

(1963) has shown that several species of *Eucalyptus* can incorporate phenylalanine into lignin and that the whole phenylpropanoid skeleton is incorporated. In this work lignin was degraded by nitrobenzene oxidation, and it was found that the two terminal carbons of the phenylpropanoid unit are converted to carbon dioxide. BARNOUD et al. (1964) have also observed incorporation of L-phenylalanine into lignin (vanillin and syringaldehyde) by tissue cultures of four different species of plants. It thus appears that plants can use phenylalanine as a source of phenylpropanoid units for lignin formation.

Possibly an intermediate between shikimic acid and phenylalanine, or tyrosine, could form lignin; but all the available data can be explained by the hypothesis that these aromatic amino acids give rise to cinnamic acid derivatives (following the action of ammonia-lyases) and that these cinnamic acid derivatives are then metabolized further, eventually giving lignin. For all practical purposes this is an irreversible process. SMITH and NEISH (1964) have demonstrated that all carbons of labelled cinnamic acid are incorporated into lignin by spruce and aspen twigs with very little incorporation into carbohydrates or proteins.

Other tracer experiments (Table 1) with several species have shown that cinnamic, *p*-coumaric, caffeic and ferulic acids were always good precursors of lignin, whereas sinapic acid was an efficient lignin precursor in those species which contain syringyl units in the lignin fraction (i.e. angiosperms). Incorporation of sinapic acid is relatively poor in gymnosperms, as expected, although HIGUCHI (1962) noted a fair incorporation in tissue cultures of *Pinus strobus*, indicating a demethoxylation reaction. Finally, coniferin has been shown to be an excellent precursor of lignin in spruce (Table 1) which indicates reduction of the carboxyl groups of cinnamic derivatives prior to polymerization to lignin.

Certain hydroxybenzoic acid derivatives showed a fair degree of incorporation to lignin, but there is no actual proof that these units were part of the lignin molecule; most C_6C_1 compounds are poorly incorporated as are also certain phenylpropanoid units such as phenylglyceric acids and *m*-methoxycinnamic acid.

Fig. 6 gives a hypothetical outline for the formation of cinnamic acid derivatives from phenylpropanoid amino acids. It has been known for some time that cinnamic acid derivatives occur mainly as esters in plants, for example, esters with quinic acid or glucose. Phenylalanine can be converted, by plants, to soluble esters of the ring-substituted cinnamic acids of Fig. 6; if these acids are administered to plants, they can readily form esters of acids with a higher degree of ring substitution or O-methylation [GEISSMAN and SWAIN, 1957; REID, 1958; McCALLA and NEISH, 1959 (2); LEVY and ZUCKER, 1960; HESS, 1964 (2); HILLIS and ISOI, 1965]. This suggests the metabolic sequence: phenylalanine → cinnamic acid → *p*-coumaric acid → caffeic acid → ferulic acid → sinapic acid. The steps in this sequence are not readily reversible so the intermediates of Fig. 6 do not form a metabolic pool in the sense that all of them are easily interconvertible. There is good evidence that methoxyl groups can be removed by plants, however, as in the conversion of syringly to guaiacyl nuclei [HIGUCHI, 1962; HIGUCHI and BROWN, 1963 (1)], although this process is less intense than the conversion of guaiacyl to syringyl nuclei. The mechanism of this "demethoxylation" is unknown, and it may be a demethylation followed by removal of a hydroxyl group. There is also good evidence for the demethylation of ferulic acid in plants [REZNIK and URBAN, 1957 (1, 2)].

LEVY and ZUCKER (1960) have suggested that cinnamyl quinate and *p*-coumaryl quinate are intermediates in formation of more highly substituted esters (e.g. chlorogenic acid). It is unlikely that the group "E" in Fig. 6 is quinic acid however, since this would give alcohol-soluble esters; recent work by EL-BASYOUNI, NEISH and TOWERS (1964) has shown that the intermediates on the direct path from phenylalanine to lignin are insoluble in hot 80% ethanol. The residue from the ethanol extraction releases the hydroxycinnamic acids on treatment with acid or alkali, and it is inferred from the conditions required for hydrolysis that the acids are bound by esterification of their carboxyl groups. When wheat plants were treated with $^{14}CO_2$ or labelled phenylalanine, the soluble esters of the cinnamic acid derivatives were only slightly labelled, whereas *p*-coumaric acid, caffeic acid and ferulic acid could be obtained by hydrolysis of the alcohol-insoluble residue and shown to be quite heavily labelled. Further work by EL-BASYOUNI and NEISH (1966) showed that these intermediates were soluble in cold buffer solutions, insoluble in cold acetone, and that they released the free acids when the acetone-insoluble residue was incubated with buffer.

Cinnamic acid itself was also esterified in the acetone-insoluble residue and was readily labelled when $^{14}CO_2$ or generally labelled L-phenylalanine were administered to the plant prior to extraction. Thus the presence of a metabolically active acetone-insoluble ester of cinnamic acid has been demonstrated in wheat and barley plants. When exogenous cinnamic acids are supplied to living plants, they label both the soluble and insoluble esters; but in this case the soluble esters are more heavily labelled than the insoluble esters, whereas the opposite is true when phenylalanine and carbon dioxide are administered. Since carbon dioxide is assimilated photosynthetically, i.e. by a completely natural process, it is likely that these insoluble esters are true natural intermediates of lignin biosynthesis and probably of other compounds related to lignin as well. It is of interest that phenylalanine, which was fed by the infusion method to a detached shoot, showed the same behaviour as carbon dioxide assimilated by photosynthesis. This is further evidence that this amino acid is a natural intermediate in lignin formation.

2. *Comparison of Species*

An interesting and unexpected result was the difference between species in incorporating aromatic amino acids into lignin. Thus, while all species tested could easily incorporate phenylalanine, relatively few could incorporate tyrosine (see Table 1). Except for a variant form of *Eucalyptus sideroxylon* (BLAND, 1963), all species which can convert tyrosine readily into lignin are members of the family *Gramineae*. This also applies to the compounds in the tyrosine and phenylalanine pools of Fig. 5. Thus *p*-hydroxyphenylpyruvic acid and *p*-hydroxyphenyllactic acid act like tyrosine in that they are only readily incorporated by species belonging to the *Gramineae* and are very poorly incorporated by other species. This species difference may be explained by a difference in the distribution of ammonia-lyases for phenylalanine and tyrosine as described in the next section.

NORD and SCHUBERT (1958) and SCHUBERT (1962) consider that *p*-hydroxyphenylpyruvate is an important intermediate in lignin biosynthesis. This hypothesis is based on a single experiment with sugar cane, a member of the *Gramineae* (ACERBO,

SCHUBERT and NORD, 1958). This α-oxo acid is a poor precursor of lignin in spruce (KRATZL and BILLEK, 1959), salvia and buckwheat (BROWN, WRIGHT and NEISH, 1959). In the light of more recent work, the most probable explanation of these observations is that *p*-hydroxyphenylpyruvate is converted to tyrosine (GAMBORG and NEISH, 1959), which then gives rise to *p*-coumaric acid under the influence of L-tyrosine ammonia-lyase (tyrase), an enzyme known to be present in sugar cane (NEISH, 1961).

C. Enzyme Studies

The first step in conversion of phenylalanine to lignin is probably the removal of ammonia by the action of L-phenylalanine ammonia-lyase (Fig. 6). This enzyme was first demonstrated by KOUKOL and CONN (1961) in barley plants. A similar enzyme named tyrase (i.e. L-tyrosine ammonia-lyase), which converts L-tyrosine to *p*-coumaric acid, was discovered by NEISH (1961). The latter enzyme is fairly active in grasses but not in legumes. A taxonomic survey of the distribution of these ammonia-lyases by YOUNG, TOWERS and NEISH (1966) has shown that they are present only in organisms which can form lignin or some cinnamic acid derivative. Thus they are found mainly in vascular plants but also occur in certain higher Basidiomycetes which are capable of forming cinnamic acid derivatives from sugars (POWER, TOWERS and NEISH, 1965).

The ammonia-lyases for phenylalanine and tyrosine are difficult to separate but appear to be two distinct enzymes (MINAMIKAWA and URITANI, 1965; YOUNG and NEISH, 1966). The phenylalanine ammonia-lyase is more stable, more widely distributed and less specific. It shows activity with a number of ring-substituted phenylalanines, especially *m*-hydroxy, *m*-fluoro and *p*-fluoro phenylalanines and some activity with the *m*-methoxy, caffeyl and guaiacyl analogues. By contrast tyrase is more specific, less susceptible to inhibition by phenolic compounds, less stable and of more restricted taxonomic distribution (YOUNG and NEISH, 1966). The enzyme active with tyrosine has been found in highest amounts in the taxonomic groups which can convert tyrosine readily into lignin (YOUNG, TOWERS and NEISH, 1966; BARNOUD et al., 1964). This was demonstrated in a striking manner by BLAND (1963) who showed that a variety of *Eucalyptus sideroxylon* could convert tyrosine into lignin whereas other species, such as *E. camaldulensis*, *E. regnans* and *E. bicostata* could not, and that this ability was correlated with the presence of tyrase in *E. sideroxylon*.

There are thus two routes for formation of *p*-coumaric acid, one by action of an ammonia-lyase on tyrosine and the other by hydroxylation of cinnamic acid. The hydroxylase catalyzing the latter reaction was demonstrated in spinach (NAIR and VINING, 1965). A further hydroxylation, which might be catalyzed by a phenolase, would give caffeic acid. This hydroxylation reaction could occur with any one of a number of esters, but for reasons stated above it is believed to occur with an ester, insoluble in ethanol or acetone, whose exact structure is not yet known. This ester is assumed to be formed following activation of the carboxyl group possibly *via* a coenzyme A ester, although it is possible that the cinnamoyl-E and *p*-coumaryl-E (Fig. 6) arise by direct transfer from the ammonia-lyases *in vivo*, the formation of the free acids *in vitro* being due to a hydrolysis which does not occur in the living cell. In any case, the fact that cinnamic acid derivatives are always found as esters in plants points to a highly developed carboxyl-activating mechanism.

Following hydroxylation, a methylation is assumed to occur, giving a ferulic acid ester. S-Adenosylmethionine: catechol O-methyltransferase (E.C. 2.1.1.6) is a well known enzyme from animal tissues. Enzymes of this type have also been demonstrated in plants. Thus FINKLE and NELSON (1963), found an enzyme in cambial scrapings of the apple tree and the woody shrub *Pittosporum crassifolia* which catalyzed methylation of caffeic acid to ferulic acid using S-adenosylmethionine as the methyl donor, FINKLE and MASRI (1964) found a similar enzyme in the Pampas grass, *Cortaderio selloana*. HESS [1964 (1, 2); 1965] showed that *Triticum* and *Petunia* contained an enzyme system which activated methionine-$^{14}CH_3$ with ATP and transferred the methyl group to a number of phenolic compounds. He was also able to prepare ferulic and sinapic acid labelled in the methoxyl groups by administering L-methionine-methyl-^{14}C to plants. These enzymes are all similar to the animal enzyme in that methylation of the catechol hydroxyl *meta* to the side chain is favored over methylation of the *p*-hydroxyl. However MANN, FALES and MUDD (1963) discovered another O-methyltransferase in plants which favored methylation of the *p*-hydroxyl. This enzyme, which was obtained from bulbs of *Nerine bowdenii*, catalyzed the methylation of norbelladine to N-isovanillyl-tyramine, a reaction which is probably important in biosynthesis of the C_6C_1—C_6C_2 alkaloids of the *Amaryllidaceae*.

Referring again to Fig. 6, further hydroxylation and methylation of ferulic acid could give rise to sinapic acid. Possibly 5-hydroxyferulic acid would function as an intermediate. This acid has not been demonstrated to occur naturally in plants, but it may yet be identified as a component of the insoluble esters. It has been synthesized, labelled with ^{14}C in the α-carbon by HIGUCHI and BROWN [1963 (2)], who showed that it could be incorporated into lignin by wheat plants, although not as readily as ferulic or sinapic acids.

In general it may be said then that the scheme for formation of cinnamic acids shown in Fig. 6 is supported not only by experiments with labelled compounds but also by enzyme studies. The main uncertainties are the actual nature of the esters which are the true intermediates and the steps involved going from ferulic to sinapic acid.

V. Cinnamyl-Alcohol Derivatives as Intermediates in Lignification

There is good evidence from experiments with ^{14}C-labelled coniferin (see Table 1) that this compound can act as a precursor of lignin in spruce. FREUDENBERG and NIEDERCORN (1958) have shown that phenylalanine can be converted to coniferin as well as to lignin in spruce twigs, and it is quite probable that this occurs by formation of ferulic acid, as shown in Fig. 6, followed by a reduction to coniferyl alcohol (Fig. 7). The experiments of FREUDENBERG et al. (1955) indicate that coniferin is enzymatically hydrolyzed to coniferyl alcohol which is then polymerized to lignin.

This dehydropolymerization, which can be done by oxidative enzymes *in vitro*, is discussed fully by Professor FREUDENBERG in this volume.

Similarly *p*-coumaric acid could be reduced to *p*-hydroxycinnamyl alcohol and sinapic acid to sinapyl alcohol (Fig. 7), and these alcohols could also undergo dehydropolymerization in conjunction with coniferyl alcohol to form lignin. FREUDENBERG and HARKIN (1963) have shown that the cambial sap of spruce contains the 4-O-glucosides of sinapyl and *p*-coumaryl alcohols, in addition to coniferin. The aldehydes would be expected to occur as intermediates in the reduction. The phloroglucinol-HCl test for lignin is believed to be due to the presence of coniferyl aldehyde units in lignin, as mentioned above. Although coniferin has not been detected in wheat plants, there is good evidence that here, also, coniferyl alcohol is an intermediate in lignin formation. HIGUCHI and BROWN [1963 (3)] found that coniferyl alcohol could dilute the intermediate formed when ferulic acid is converted to lignin. They also detected formation of coniferyl aldehyde and coniferyl alcohol from ferulic acid-2-^{14}C although no coniferin was formed. It was concluded that the formation of coniferin is not essential for lignification. The essential thing is to have a supply of coniferyl alcohol, and this may be obtained both by reduction of the widely occurring ferulic acid esters and by hydrolysis of coniferin. Both sources are available to the spruce tree, but most other plants probably generate coniferyl alcohol solely by reduction of ferulic esters. Presumably in spruce these esters are also intermediates in the biosynthesis of coniferin.

It has been suggested that eugenol is an important natural intermediate in lignin formation. SIEGEL (1955) studied the peroxidative polymerization of a number of compounds using peroxidase-containing plant tissues. He observed that eugenol gave a substance very much like lignin. HIGUCHI (1957) carried out similar experiments using plant materials and a crude peroxidase preparation. Freshly distilled eugenol did not form lignin but, on standing, eugenol apparently undergoes an autooxidation to form coniferyl aldehyde. This aldehyde forms a lignin-like polymer similar to that obtained from coniferyl alcohol. STAFFORD [1960 (1)] studied the polymerization of eugenol and other compounds by tissues of timothy grass (*Phleum pratense*). Eugenol, even when freshly distilled, gave a lignin-like polymer in small amounts. Under the same conditions, however, ferulic acid gave a polymer much more similar to the alkali-soluble lignin of timothy grass. It is probable that eugenol is of little, if any, importance as a precursor of protolignin. However, there is a possibility that ferulic acid is incorporated directly into the lignin of young grasses and this may account for the complete solubility of these lignins in dilute alkali [BONDI and MEYER, 1948; STAFFORD, 1960 (1, 2), 1962, 1965].

VI. Compounds Biogenetically-Related to Lignin

Studies with ^{14}C-labelled compounds have shown that other phenylpropanoid compounds, as well as some which are not so obviously phenylpropanoid, can be derived, at least in part, from phenylalanine or tyrosine. These include flavonoids, coumarins, acetophenones, hydroxybenzoic acids, esters and glucosides of hydroxylated cinnamic and benzoic acids and alcohols, certain alkaloids and a few secondary metabolic products of lichens or fungi. Lack of space does not permit a detailed review of this work, but it is of interest to summarize it in relation to lignin formation (Fig. 8). Reviews by REZNIK (1960), GRISEBACH (1961), NEISH [1964 (1, 2), 1966], SWAIN (1962) and BATTERSBY (1963) can be consulted for further details; and only a few pertinent recent papers will be cited here.

Some of the compounds mentioned in Fig. 8 appear to be fairly closely related to lignin since they are formed from cinnamic acid derivatives. However, there are a number of aromatic secondary metabolites which can be derived from one or the other of the phenylpropanoid amino acids but not from cinnamic acid derivatives. Examples are the phenylethyl amine alkaloids, which appear to arise from decarboxylation products, and the fungal terphenylquinone, volucrisporin, which is probably formed from phenylpyruvate or *m*-hydroxyphenylpyruvate (READ, VINING and HASKINS, 1962). The lichen substance, pulvinic dilactone, is formed from phenylalanine but not from cinnamic acid (MAASS, TOWERS and NEISH, 1964), and the labelling pattern suggests a terphenylquinone intermediate. However, most of the phenylpropanoid substances found in vascular plants appear to be derived from cinnamic acids [NEISH, 1964 (1, 2)].

Work in several laboratories has established that flavonoids, anthocyanins and isoflavones contain a phenylpropanoid unit derived from phenylalanine *via* cinnamic acid derivatives. The pattern of oxygen substitution in the B-ring is usually the same as one or other of the cinnamic acid derivatives in Fig. 6. It has been known for some time that the pattern of ring-substitution in anthocyanins is controlled genetically (ALSTON, 1964). HESS [1964 (2), 1965] has studied genotypes of *Petunia* differing in their ability to methylate the B-ring of their anthocyanins and has concluded that the genetic control is not on the methylation reaction but rather on selection of the already-methylated cinnamic acid derivative for anthocyanin formation. In other words, all genotypes could be visualized as having a pool of cinnamic acid derivatives, such as is shown in Fig. 6, but differing in their ability to select one of the pool components for anthocyanin biosynthesis.

This pool could also supply precursors of coumarins. Some of the most widely-distributed coumarins can be obtained by *ortho*-hydroxylation of one of the intermediates in this pool, followed by *trans* → *cis* isomerization. Pungenin, a 3,4-dihydroxyacetophenone glucoside, is probably formed from caffeic acid by reactions involving decarboxylation (NEISH, 1959). Transesterification from the intermediates of Fig. 6 could give rise to cinnamoyl quinates, such as chlorogenic acid, or 1-cinnamoyl glucose esters. HILLIS and ISOI (1965) have shown that a number of cinnamoyl esters, flavonoids and stilbenes can be formed from phenylalanine by shoots of eucalyptus. There is good evidence that hydroxybenzoic acids can be formed in plants by β-oxidation of the corresponding cinnamic acids (GRISEBACH and VOLLMER, 1963; EL-BASYOUNI et al., 1964; ZENK and MÜLLER, 1964; ZENK, 1964; KINDL and BILLEK, 1964). It is also possible that hydroxybenzoic acids may arise from intermediates of the shikimic pathway of Fig. 4 (CONN and SWAIN, 1961; GIBSON and GIBSON, 1964).

Cinnamic acid derivatives have also recently been implicated as intermediates in the synthesis of the C_6C_1—C_6C_2 alkaloids of the *Amaryllidaceae*, where they contribute a C_6C_1 unit, presumably formed by β-oxidation [SUHADOLNIK and ZULALIAN, 1963; ZULALIAN and SUHADOLNIK, 1964; BATTERSBY et al., 1964 (1)]. In addition,

BATTERSBY et al. [1964 (2)] have found that a phenylpropanoid unit of colchicine is derived completely from phenylalanine, quite possibly *via* a cinnamic acid derivative.

One of the main functions of the cinnamic esters of Fig. 6 is to supply units for the biosynthesis of lignin. Reduction to the corresponding alcohols (coniferyl, *p*-coumaryl and sinapyl alcohols) can give the substrates needed for dehydropolymerization to lignin. These alcohols may undergo other reactions such as formation of glycosides or dimerization to lignans. Although there are no reports of tracer experiments on biosynthesis of lignans, it may be inferred from the structures of these naturally-occurring phenylpropanoid dimers (HEARON and MAC GREGOR, 1955; ERDTMAN, 1955; HATHWAY, 1962) that they could easily be formed from coniferyl alcohol or related compounds by a stereospecific coupling reaction. It is expected that this would be catalyzed by quite different enzymes than those causing the dehydropolymerization to lignin. The naturally-occurring lignans are all optically active phenylpropanoid dimers. Trimers of this type have not been found in nature. These facts support the hypothesis that natural lignans are formed by a reductive coupling (NEISH, 1966). On the other hand, the dehydropolymerization of coniferyl alcohol is a free radical reaction which gives optically inactive products, and dimers are obtained only as fleeting intermediates. However, it is probable that lignin and lignans are closely related in biosynthesis as well as in name since both may arise from substituted cinnamyl alcohols (NEISH, 1966).

VII. Evolution of Lignification

As mentioned in the Introduction, lignin formation is characteristic of vascular plants. It serves to distinguish them from other plants and, indeed, from all other organisms. The position of lignin in relation to evolution in the plant kingdom is therefore of considerable interest. The outline of the evolution of plants shown in Fig. 9 emphasizes the fact that simple plants, such as the fungi, algae and mosses, do not possess tracheids. The first group of plants which are believed to have had tracheids are the *Psilophytales*, which were common in the Devonian period. It is believed that these plants originated from a simpler progenitor which was derived from a green alga and that, in turn, other groups of vascular plants have originated from the *Psilophytales* (LAWRENCE, 1960). It appears that there is a sudden discontinuity in evolution between plants possessing tracheids and those not having them, and from this one may infer that the ability to produce lignin was acquired rather suddenly in terms of the geological time scale.

In discussing the origin of lignin, it is convenient to distinguish between primary and secondary metabolism of plants. The primary metabolites may be defined as substances which are common to all living cells and are necessary for such essential processes as the biosynthesis of nucleic acids, lipids, carbohydrates and proteins. On the other hand there are a great many naturally-occurring compounds which are not found in all organisms and which may be termed "secondary metabolites". Some of these, which are found only in a few species, include certain terpenes, alkaloids and phenolic compounds. Although these secondary metabolites may be of great value to the plant in which they are found, they are not essential for life.

HOROWITZ (1945) has proposed an interesting theory which accounts for the evolution of biosynthetic pathways for primary metabolites, such as phenylalanine. The first organisms were assumed to have evolved in the presence of a complex mixture of preformed organic compounds in the primitive oceans. They had very limited biosynthetic powers; but as the organic compounds in the oceans were used

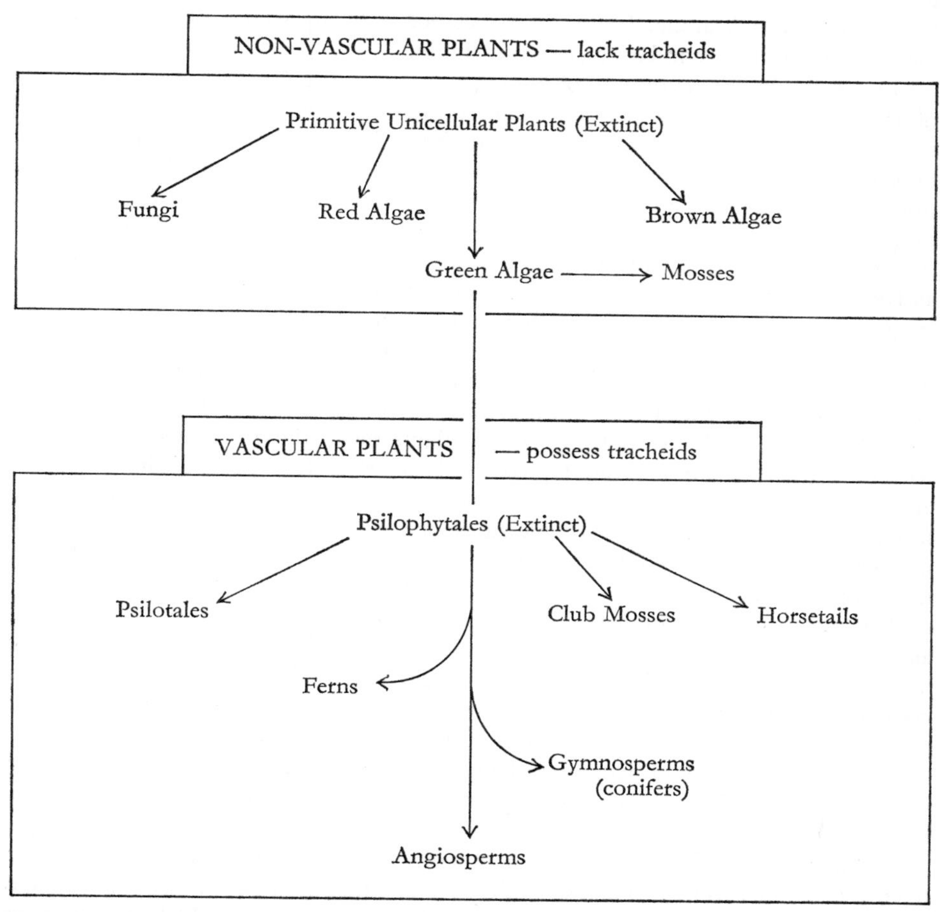

Fig. 9. Simplified outline of evolution in the plant kingdom. It is assumed that all living organisms are descended from a single cell and, therefore, that all plants have a common, primitive, unicellular ancestor. Early lines of evolution presumably originated among very simple plants which are now extinct and have left no clear fossil record

up, mutants with increased biosynthetic powers would be expected to replace the parent organisms. One can imagine the biosynthetic pathway for phenylalanine, shown in Fig. 4, to have evolved, step by step, working backwards from phenylalanine to carbohydrates.

A similar line of reasoning can be used to explain the origin of biosynthetic pathways for all primary metabolites. However, the case with secondary metabolites is rather different. They have presumably developed at a much later period when primitive earth conditions favoring the origin of life had disappeared. These metabolites were probably developed by biochemically-competent organisms, and it is more reasonable to assume that their biosynthetic pathways are either extensions of pathways for synthesis of primary metabolites or branches from them. As far as the formation of lignin is concerned, it is probably an extension of the pathway for synthesis of phenylalanine. The primary metabolite, phenylalanine, thus becomes the main source of the secondary metabolite, lignin.

In considering the evolution of lignification, one must also consider the problem of excretion in plants. Even the simplest organisms accumulate unwanted substances which are excreted into the surrounding medium. This process is facilitated by the large surface of microorganisms, in relation to their volume. During evolution, however, as larger and larger organisms were formed, the surface-to-volume ratio became less and less favorable for excretion into the surrounding medium. Animals have solved this problem by development of a complex circulatory system and special organs for elimination of waste products; their waste products are frequently converted to more soluble or less toxic substances prior to excretion. However the higher plants do not have an efficient system for external excretion; they depend primarily on the chemical transformation of metabolic by-products to volatile, insoluble or non-toxic compounds. Excretion can occur from the roots or onto the surface of leaves but, in general, plants retain these secondary substances within their bodies and practise a type of local excretion (Reznik, 1960) into vacuoles and cell walls. This probably explains the wide variety of secondary metabolites found in higher plants. Water-soluble substances like anthocyanins may accumulate in vacuoles whereas insoluble phenolic compounds such as lignin may be deposited in the cell walls.

Secondary metabolites may be beneficial to the organism (Fraenkel, 1959), although they are not essential for the manifestation of life. For example, a secondary metabolite might attract insects to the flowers, thus aiding pollination; it might contribute to the survival of the plant by repelling harmful insects or making the plant unpalatable for herbivorous animals; or a secondary substance might accumulate which would make the plant less susceptible to attack by parasites or which might enable the plant to better resist adverse conditions such as frost or drought.

During the course of evolution a mutant which differed from the parent by having the ability to form some secondary metabolite might have a slight advantage in survival over the parent and would thus ultimately replace it. With this in mind one can visualize how the biogenesis of lignin and related phenolic compounds may have originated. The first step would probably depend on the formation of cinnamic acid from phenylalanine. This change, which only requires that one additional enzyme be produced, would represent a sudden transition in metabolism. It can be imagined that such a mutation occurred in some primitive ancestor of vascular plants with limited powers of excretion. This does not necessarily mean that free cinnamic acid would accumulate since it might be esterified, due to the action of enzymes already present for other more vital functions such as synthesis of lipids, proteins, nucleic acids and carbohydrates. A number of esters of cinnamic acid may have accumulated instead, to give a mutant strain with a slight advantage in survival over the parent. Accumulation of a variety of esters is likely since enzymes involved in the synthesis and hydrolysis of esters generally have a rather broad substrate specificity.

A further mutation could occur, eventually, which would result in conversion of one of the secondary substances to a new group of compounds, e.g. hydroxylation to the corresponding *p*-coumaric acid derivatives. This might result at once in the ability to synthesize lignin, because phenolase, peroxidase, methyltransferases and enzymes capable of reducing the esterified carboxyl group might already have been present, since they are found today in organisms which cannot form lignin. In other words, during evolution of vascular plants acquisition of the ability to make L-phenylalanine ammonialyase and possibly a phenylhydroxylase may have been the only mutations needed to make possible the formation of lignin from carbohydrates. Once this ability was acquired, the ultimate development of tracheids, vessels and fibers became possible, and lignin was *no longer a waste material*, but rather a substance necessary for the evolutionary development of higher plants. The ability of lignin to strengthen and reduce the wettability of cellulose walls is considered to be essential for large erect terrestrial plants.

It is rather satisfying for a botanist to speculate that the failure of plants to develop a complex system of organs for external excretion as was done by animals, instead of limiting the size of the plant body, has actually made possible the evolution of trees, the tallest and most enduring of all living things. This evolution was possible since retention of cinnamic acid derivatives in the plant body set the stage for development of biosynthetic pathways leading to lignin.

VIII. Summary

Tracer and enzyme studies on the formation of lignin in plants support the hypothetical sequence: carbohydrates → shikimic acid → phenylalanine → cinnamic acid derivatives → cinnamyl alcohol derivatives → lignin. In addition, some species, especially grasses, can utilize tyrosine for formation of the cinnamic acid derivatives (Fig. 6). Phenylalanine and tyrosine are probably formed in plants by a pathway similar to, and possibly identical with, the pathway established for microorganisms (Fig. 4). A number of other phenolic substances found in plants can arise from the same cinnamic acid derivatives that are intermediates in lignin formation (Figs. 6 and 8). The exact nature of these intermediates remains to be established. They are polar substances, probably esters, which are insoluble in ethanol or acetone. Lignin arises as a result of their reduction to the corresponding cinnamyl alcohols (Fig. 7). Phylogenetic development of the ability to form lignin can be visualized as a result of the acquisition of phenylalanine and tyrosine ammonia-lyases and phenylhydroxylase by plants.

IX. References

ACERBO, S. N., W. J. SCHUBERT, and F. F. NORD: Investigations on lignins and lignification. XIX. The mode of incorporation of *p*-hydroxyphenylpyruvic acid into lignin. J. Am. Chem. Soc. **80**, 1990—1992 (1958).

— — — Investigations on lignins and lignification. XXII. The conversion of D-glucose into lignin in Norway spruce. J. Am. Chem. Soc. **82**, 735—739 (1960).

ADLER, E., K. J. BJÖRKVIST, and S. HÄGGROTH: Über die Ursache der Farbreaktionen des Holzes. Acta Chem. Scand. **2**, 93—94 (1948).

ALSTON, R. E.: The genetics of phenolic compounds. In: Biochemistry of phenolic compounds, pp. 171—204. Edited by HARBORNE, J. B. London: Academic Press 1964.

ALTERMATT, H., and A. C. NEISH: Die Bildung von Cellulose und Xylan aus radioaktiven Monosacchariden in Weizenpflanzen. Chimia (Switz.) **10**, 157—164 (1956).

BALINSKY, D., and D. D. DAVIES: (1) Aromatic biosynthesis in higher plants. I. Preparation and properties of dehydroshikimic reductase. Biochem. J. **80**, 292—296 (1961).

— — (2) Aromatic biosynthesis in higher plants. II. Mode of attachment of shikimic acid and dehydroshikimic acid to dehydroshikimic reductase. Biochem. J. **80**, 296—300 (1961).

— — (3) Aromatic biosynthesis in higher plants. III. Preparation and properties of dehydroquinase. Biochem. J. **80**, 300—304 (1961).

BARNOUD, F., T. HIGUCHI, J.-P. JOSELEAU, and A. MOLLARD: La biosynthèse des lignines dans les tissus végétaux cultivés *in vitro*: role de précurseur de la L-phénylalanine. Compt. rend. **259**, 4339—4341 (1964).

BATE-SMITH, E. C.: Commoner phenolic constituents of plants and their systematic distribution. Sci. Proc. Roy. Dublin Soc. **27**, 165—176 (1956).

— The simple polyphenolic constituents of plants. In: Wood extractives, pp. 133—158. Edited by HILLIS, W. E. New York: Academic Press 1962.

BATTERSBY, A. R.: The biosynthesis of alkaloids (Tilden Lecture). Proc. Chem. Soc. **1963**, 189—200.

—, R. BINKS, S. W. BREUER, H. M. FALES, W. C. WILDMAN, and R. J. HIGHET: (1) Alkaloid biosynthesis. Part III. Amaryllidaceae alkaloids: The biosynthesis of lycorine and its relatives. J. Chem. Soc. **1964**, 1595—1609.

— —, J. J. REYNOLDS, and D. A. YEOWELL: Alkaloid biosynthesis. Part VI. The biosynthesis of colchicine. J. Chem. Soc. **1964**, 4257—4268.

BLAND, D. E.: Lignification in *Eucalyptus*. Incorporation of phenylalanine, tyrosine and methionine into *Eucalyptus sideroxylon* and *Eucalyptus camaldulensis*. Biochem. J. **88**, 523—525 (1963).

BONDI, A., and H. MEYER: Lignins in young plants. Biochem. J. **43**, 248—256 (1948).

BRAUNS, F. E., and D. A. BRAUNS: The chemistry of lignin (supplement volume). New York: Academic Press 1960.

BREWER, C. P., L. M. COOKE, and H. HIBBERT: Studies on lignin and related compounds. LXXXIV. The high pressure hydrogenation of maple wood: hydrol lignin. J. Am. Chem. Soc. **70**, 57—59 (1948).

BROWN, S. A.: Studies on lignin biosynthesis using isotopic carbon. IX. Taxonomic distribution of the ability to utilize tyrosine in lignification. Can. J. Botany **39**, 253—258 (1961).

— Lignin and tannin biosynthesis. In: Biochemistry of phenolic compounds, pp. 361—398. Edited by HARBORNE, J. B. London: Academic Press 1964.

—, and A. C. NEISH: (1) Shikimic acid as a precursor in lignin biosynthesis. Nature **175**, 688—690 (1955).

— — (2) Studies of lignin biosynthesis using isotopic carbon. IV. Formation from some aromatic monomers. Can. J. Biochem. and Physiol. **33**, 948—962 (1955).

— — Studies of lignin biosynthesis using isotopic carbon. V. Comparative studies on different plant species. Can. J. Biochem. and Physiol. **34**, 769—778 (1956).

— — Studies of lignin biosynthesis using isotopic carbon. VIII. Isolation of radioactive hydrogenolysis products of lignins. J. Am. Chem. Soc. **81**, 2419—2424 (1959).

—, D. WRIGHT, and A. C. NEISH: Studies of lignin biosynthesis using isotopic carbon. VII. The role of *p*-hydroxyphenylpyruvic acid. Can. J. Biochem. and Physiol. **37**, 25—34 (1959).

CONN, E. E.: Enzymology of phenolic biosynthesis. In: Biochemistry of phenolic compounds, pp. 399—435. Edited by HARBORNE, J. B. London: Academic Press 1964.

—, and T. SWAIN: Biosynthesis of gallic acid in higher plants. Chem. and Ind. (London) **1961**, 592—593.

Coscia, C. J., M. I. Ramirez, W. J. Schubert, and F. F. Nord: Investigations on lignins and lignification. XXVI. Studies on the utilization of pyruvate in lignification. Biochemistry **1**, 447—451 (1962).

Cramer, A. B., M. J. Hunter, and H. Hibbert: Studies on lignin and related compounds. XXXV. The ethanolysis of spruce wood. J. Am. Chem. Soc. **61**, 509—516 (1939).

Creighton, R. H. J., R. D. Gibbs, and H. Hibbert: Studies on lignin and related compounds. LXXV. Alkaline nitrobenzene oxidation of plant materials and application to taxonomic classification. J. Am. Chem. Soc. **66**, 32—37 (1944).

Davis, B. D.: Intermediates in amino acid biosynthesis. Advances in Enzymol. **16**, 247—312 (1955).

— On the importance of being ionized. Arch. Biochem. Biophys. **78**, 497—509 (1958).

Dixon, M., and E. C. Webb: Enzymes. London: Longmans, Green & Co. Ltd. 1964.

Eberhardt, G., and W. J. Schubert: Investigations on lignin and lignification. XVII. Evidence for the mediation of shikimic acid in the biogenesis of lignin building stones. J. Am. Chem. Soc. **78**, 2835—2837 (1956).

El-Basyouni, S. Z., and A. C. Neish: Occurrence of metabolically-active bound forms of cinnamic acid and its phenolic derivatives in acetone powders of wheat and barley plants. Phytochemistry **5** 683—691 (1966).

— —, and G. H. N. Towers: The phenolic acids in wheat. III. Insoluble derivatives of phenolic cinnamic acids as natural intermediates in lignin biosynthesis. Phytochemistry **3**, 627—639 (1964).

—, D. Chen, R. K. Ibrahim, A. C. Neish, and G. H. N. Towers: The biosynthesis of hydroxybenzoic acids in higher plants. Phytochemistry **3**, 485—492 (1964).

Erdtman, H.: Lignans. In: Modern methods of plant analysis, Vol. III, pp. 428—449. Edited by Paech, K., and M. V. Tracey. Berlin-Göttingen-Heidelberg: Springer 1955.

Esau, K.: Plant anatomy. Chapter 11 (Xylem), pp. 221—264. New York: John Wiley and Sons, Inc. 1953.

Finkle, B. J., and M. S. Masri: Methylation of polyhydroxyaromatic compounds by pampas grass *O*-methyltransferase. Biochim. Biophys. Acta **85**, 167—169 (1964).

—, and R. F. Nelson: Enzyme reactions with phenolic compounds: a *meta-O*-methyltransferase in plants. Biochim. Biophys. Acta **78**, 747—749 (1963).

Flaig, W.: Zur Umwandlung von Lignins in Huminstoffe. Freiberger Forschungsh. **A254**, 39—56 (1962).

Fraenkel, G. S.: The raison d'être of secondary plant substances. Science **129**, 1466—1470 (1959).

Freudenberg, K., and J. M. Harkin: The glucosides of cambial sap of spruce. Phytochemistry **2**, 189—193 (1963).

—, W. Lautsch und K. Engler: Lignin. XXXIV. Die Bildung von Vanillin aus Fichtenlignin. Ber. deut. chem. Ges. **73B**, 167—171 (1940).

—, u. B. Lehman: Untersuchungen eines mit ^{14}C markierten Ligninpräparates. Chem. Ber. **96**, 1850—1854 (1963).

—, u. F. Niedercorn: Anwendung radioaktiver Isotope bei der Erforschung des Lignins. VIII. Umwandlung des Phenylalanins in Coniferin und Fichtenlignin. Chem. Ber. **91**, 591—597 (1958).

—, H. Reznik, W. Fuchs und M. Reichert: Untersuchungen über die Entstehung des Lignins und des Holzes. Naturwissenschaften **42**, 29—35 (1955).

Gamborg, O. L., and A. C. Neish: Biosynthesis of phenylalanine and tyrosine in young wheat and buckwheat plants. Can. J. Biochem. and Physiol. **37**, 1277—1285 (1959).

—, and L. R. Wetter: An aromatic amino acid transaminase from mung bean. Can. J. Biochem. and Physiol. **41**, 1733—1740 (1963).

— —, and A. C. Neish: The oxidation of some aromatic α-hydroxy acids by glycollate: O_2 oxidoreductase. Phytochemistry **1**, 159—168 (1962).

Geissman, T. A., and T. Swain: Biosynthesis of flavonoid compounds in higher plants. Chem & Ind. (London) **1957**, 984.

Gibson, F.: Chorismic acid: Purification and some chemical and physical studies. Biochem. J. **90**, 256—261 (1964).

GIBSON, M. I., and F. GIBSON: Preliminary studies on the isolation and metabolism of an intermediate in aromatic biosynthesis: Chorismic acid. Biochem. J. **90**, 248—256 (1964).
GIBSON, F., and L. M. JACKMAN: Structure of chorismic acid, a new intermediate in aromatic biosynthesis. Nature **198**, 388—389 (1963).
GOLDSCHMID, O., and G. R. QUIMBY: Lignin precursors. The role of quinic acid. Tappi **47**, 528—533 (1964).
GRISEBACH, H.: The biosynthesis of isoflavones. In: Chemistry of natural phenolic compounds, pp. 59—73. Edited by OLLIS, W. D. London: Pergamon Press 1961.
—, u. K.-O. VOLLMER: Untersuchungen zur Biosynthese des Salicylsäuremethylesters in *Gaultheria procumbens* L. Z. Naturforsch. **18b**, 753—756 (1963).
HASEGAWA, M.: Alicylic acid precursors of polyphenols. In: Wood extractives, pp. 263 to 276. Edited by HILLIS, W. E. New York: Academic Press 1962.
—, and T. HIGUCHI: Formation of lignin from glucose in eucalyptus tree. J. Japan. Forestry Soc. **42**, 305—308 (1960).
— —, and H. ISHIKAWA: Formation of lignin in tissue culture of *Pinus strobus*. Plant Cell Physiol. **1**, 173—182 (1960).
HATHWAY, D. E.: The lignans. In: Wood extractives, pp. 159—190. Edited by HILLIS, W. E. New York: Academic Press 1962.
HEARON, W. M., and W. S. MACGREGOR: The naturally occurring lignans. Chem. Revs. **55**, 957—1068 (1955).
HESS, D.: (1) Methionin als Methylgruppendonator für Zimtsäuren und Anthocyane. Z. Naturforsch. **19b**, 148—150 (1964).
— (2) Der Einbau Methylgruppen-markierter Ferulasäure und Sinapinsäure in die Anthocyane von *Petunia hybrida*. Planta **60**, 568—581 (1964).
— (3) Die Methylierung von Kaffeesäure zu Ferulasäure durch Enzymsysteme aus höheren Pflanzen. Z. Naturforsch. **19b**, 447—449 (1964).
— Vergleich der methylierenden Potenzen von Genotypen mit verschiedenartig methylierten Anthocyanen im zellfreien System. Z. Pflanzenphysiol. **53**, 1—18 (1965).
HIBBERT, H.: Lignin. Ann. Rev. Biochem. **11**, 183—202 (1942).
HIGUCHI, T.: Biochemical studies of lignin formation. II. Physiol. Plantarum **10**, 621—632 (1957).
— Studies of lignin biosynthesis using isotopic carbon. X. Formation of lignin from phenylpropanoids in tissue culture of white pine. Can. J. Biochem. and Physiol. **40**, 31—34 (1962).
—, and S. A. BROWN: (1) Studies of lignin biosynthesis using isotopic carbon. XI. Reactions relating to lignification in young wheat plants. Can. J. Biochem. and Physiol. **41**, 65—76 (1963).
— — (2) Studies of lignin biosynthesis using isotopic carbon. XII. The biosynthesis and metabolism of sinapic acid. Can. J. Biochem. and Physiol. **41**, 613—620 (1963).
— — (3) Studies of lignin biosynthesis using isotopic carbon. XIII. The phenylpropanoid system in lignification. Can. J. Biochem. Physiol. **41**, 621—628 (1963).
—, F. BARNOUD et A. ROBERT: La biosynthèse des lignines. Assoc. tech. ind. papetière, Bull. **18**, 92—106 (1964).
HILLIS, W. E., and K. ISOI: The biosynthesis of polyphenols in *Eucalyptus* species. Phytochemistry **4**, 905—918 (1965).
HOROWITZ, N. H.: The evolution of biochemical syntheses. Proc. Nat. Acad. Sci. US **31**, 153—157 (1945).
IBRAHIM, R. K., and G. H. N. TOWERS: The identification, by chromatography, of plant phenolic acids. Arch. Biochem. Biophys. **87**, 125—128 (1960).
JONES, J. D., A. C. HULME, and L. S. C. WOOLTORTON: The use of polyvinylpyrrolidone in the isolation of enzymes from apple fruits. Phytochemistry **4**, 659—676 (1965).
KINDL, H., u. G. BILLEK: Zur Biosynthese der Benzosäuren. Monatsh. Chem. **95**, 1044 bis 1052 (1964).
KOUKOL, J., and E. E. CONN: The metabolism of aromatic compounds in higher plants. IV. Purification and properties of the phenylalanine deaminase of *Hordeum vulgare*. J. Biol. Chem. **236**, 2692—2698 (1961).
KRATZL, K.: Zur Biogenese des Lignins. Holz Roh- u. Werkstoff **19**, 219—232 (1961).

— Lignin — its biochemistry and structure. In: Cellular ultrastructure of woody plants, pp. 157—180. Edited by Côte, W. A. Syracuse, N.Y.: Syracuse University Press 1965.

—, u. G. Billek: Über das Verhalten der 4-Hydroxyphenylbrenztraubensäure in verholzenden Gewebe der Fichte. Monatsh. Chem. **90**, 536—543 (1959).

—, u. H. Czepel: Untersuchung der Äthanolyseprodukte von Fichtenholzlignin mit Hilfe der Gaschromatographie. Monatsh. Chem. **95**, 1609—1612 (1964).

—, u. H. Faigle: Über das Verhalten von markiertem Coniferin in der verholzenden Pflanze. III. Monatsh. Chem. **89**, 708—715 (1958).

— — Der Einbau von D-Glucose-1-^{14}C in das Phenylpropangerüst des Fichtenlignins. Monatsh. Chem. **90**, 768—770 (1959).

— — Die Biogenese der Phenylpropan-Einheit des Fichtenlignins. Z. Naturforsch. **15b**, 4—11 (1960).

—, u. G. Hofbauer: Über das Verhalten von markiertem Coniferin in der verholzenden Pflanze. II. Monatsh. Chem. **89**, 96—101 (1958).

—, u. J. Zauner: Über den biologischen Einbau von ^{14}C markiertem Xylit in Holz und seine Konstituenten. Holzforschung **14**, 108—111 (1962).

—, G. Billek, E. Klein und K. Buchtela: Über das Verhalten von markiertem Coniferin in der verholzenden Pflanze. I. Monatsh. Chem. **88**, 721—734 (1957).

—, W. Kisser, A. Graf und G. Hofbauer: Studien zum biologischen Aufbau der Seitenkette von Phenylpropanen. Monatsh. Chem. **90**, 526—535 (1959).

Kretovich, V. L., and Zh. v. Uspenskaya: Synthesis of phenylalanine from phenylpyruvic acid in homogenates of pea sprouts. Biokhimiya **23**, 248—253 (1958).

Lawrence, G. H. M.: Taxonomy of vascular plants. Fifth printing, p. 138. New York: Macmillan Co. 1960.

Levy, C. C., and M. Zucker: Cinnamyl and *p*-coumaryl esters as intermediates in the biosynthesis of chlorogenic acid. J. Biol. Chem. **235**, 2418—2425 (1960).

Maass, W. S. G., G. H. N. Towers und A. C. Neish: Flechtenstoffe: I. Untersuchungen zur Biogenese des Pulvinsäureanhydrids. Ber. deut. botan. Ges. **77**, 157—161 (1964).

Mann, J. D., H. M. Fales, and S. H. Mudd: Alkaloids and plant metabolism. VI. *O*-methylation *in vitro* of norbelladine, a precursor of amaryllidaceae alkaloids. J. Biol. Chem. **238**, 3820—3823 (1963).

Maüle, C.: Das Verhalten verholzter Membranen gegen Kalium permanganat, ein Holzreaktionen neuer Art. Beitr. wiss. Bot. **4**, 166—185 (1901).

McCalla, D. R., and A. C. Neish: (1) Metabolism of phenylpropanoid compounds in *Salvia*. I. Biosynthesis of phenylalanine and tyrosine. Can. J. Biochem. and Physiol. **37**, 531—536 (1959).

— — (2) Metabolism of phenylpropanoid compounds in *Salvia*. II. Biosynthesis of phenolic cinnamic acids. Can. J. Biochem. and Physiol. **37**, 537—547 (1959).

Minamikawa, T., and I. Uritani: Phenylalanine ammonia-lyase in sliced sweet potato roots. J. Biochem. (Tokyo) **57**, 678—688 (1965).

Mitsuhashi, S., and B. D. Davis: Aromatic biosynthesis. XII. Conversion of 5-dehydroquinic acid to 5-dehydroshikimic acid by 5-dehydroquinase. Biochem. et Biophys. Acta **15**, 54—61 (1954).

Nair, P. M., and L. C. Vining: Cinnamic acid hydroxylase in spinach. Phytochemistry **4**, 161—168 (1965).

Nandy, M., and N. C. Ganguli: (1) Studies on 5-dehydroshikimic reductase from mung bean seedlings (*Phaseolus aureus*). Arch. Biochem. Biophys. **92**, 399—408 (1961).

— — (2) Biological synthesis of 5-dehydroshikimic acid by a plant extract. Biochim. Biophys. Acta **48**, 608—610 (1961).

Neish, A. C.: The biosynthesis of cell wall carbohydrates. II. Formation of cellulose and xylan from labelled monosaccharides in wheat plants. Can. J. Biochem. and Physiol. **33**, 658—666 (1955).

— Biosynthesis of pungenin from C^{14}-labelled compounds by colorado spruce. Can. J. Botany **37**, 1085—1100 (1959).

— The formation of *m*- and *p*-coumaric acids by enzymatic deamination of the corresponding isomers of tyrosine. Phytochemistry **1**, 1—24 (1961).

— (1) Cinnamic acid derivatives as intermediates in the biosynthesis of lignin and related compounds. In: Formation of wood in forest trees, pp. 219—239. Edited by ZIMMERMANN, M. H. New York: Academic Press 1964.
— (2) Major pathways of biosynthesis of phenols. In: Biochemistry of phenolic compounds, pp. 295—359. Edited by HARBORNE, J. B. London: Academic Press 1964.
— Coumarins, phenylpropanes and lignin. In: Plant biochemistry. Edited by BONNER, J., and J. VARNER. New York: Academic Press 1966.
NORD, F. F.: On the biochemistry of lignin. Tappi **47**, 624—628 (1964).
—, and W. J. SCHUBERT: Lignification. Proc. Intern. Congr. Biochem., 4th Congr. Vienna, 1958. Vol. 2, pp. 189—206. titled Biochemistry of Wood. Edited by KRATZL, K., and G. BILLEK. London: Pergamon Press 1959.
PAYEN, A., and J. F. PERSOZ: Ann. chim. et phys. **53**, 73 (1833). In: Enzymes by DIXON, M., and E. C. WEBB, p. 1. London: Longmans, Green & Co. Ltd. 1964.
POWER, D. M., G. H. N. TOWERS, and A. C. NEISH: Biosynthesis of phenolic acids by certain wood-destroying basidiomycetes. Can. J. Biochem. **43**, 1397—1407 (1965).
READ, G., L. C. VINING, and R. H. HASKINS: Biogenetic studies on volucrisporin. Can J. Chem. **40**, 2357—2361 (1962).
REID, W. W.: Biosynthesis of scopoletin and caffeic acid in *Nicotiana tabacum*. Chem. & Ind. (London) **1958**, 1439—1440.
REZNIK, H.: Vergleichende Biochemie der Phenylpropane. Ergeb. Biol. **23**, 14—46 (1960).
—, u. R. URBAN: (1) Über den Metabolismus ^{14}C-markierter Ferulasäure im Pflanzenversuch. Naturwissenschaften **44**, 13 (1957).
— — (2) Über den Metabolismus ^{14}C-markierter Ferulasäure im Pflanzenversuch. II. Beiträge zur Biogenese der Flavonoide. Naturwissenschaften **44**, 592—593 (1957).
SCHUBERT, W. J.: Lignin formation. In: Methods in enzymology, V., pp. 402—408. Edited by COLOWICK, S. P., and N. O. KAPLAN. New York: Academic Press 1962.
SCHÜTTE, H. R., and R. FREYER: Aromatische Aminosäuren als Vorstufen des Lignins. Flora (Jena) **155**, 511—514 (1965).
SHIBATA, S., and M. YAMAZAKI: The biogenesis of rutin. Pharm. Bull. (Tokyo) **5**, 501—502 (1957); C.A. **52**, 13882 (1958).
SIEGEL, S. M.: The biochemistry of lignin formation. Physiol. Plantarum **8**, 20—32 (1955).
SMITH, D. G., and A. C. NEISH: Alkaline oxidation of ^{14}C-labelled protolignin formed from cinnamic acid in spruce and aspen twigs. Phytochemistry **3**, 609—615 (1964).
SPRINSON, D. B.: The biosynthesis of aromatic compounds from D-glucose. Advances in Carbohydrate Chem. **15**, 235—270 (1960).
STAFFORD, H. A.: (1) Differences between lignin-like polymers formed by peroxidation of eugenol and ferulic acid in leaf sections of *Phleum*. Plant Physiol. **35**, 108—114 (1960).
— (2) Comparison of lignin-like polymers produced peroxidatively by cinnamic acid derivatives in leaf sections of *Phleum*. Plant Physiol. **35**, 612—618 (1960).
— Histochemical & biochemical differences between lignin-like materials in *Phleum pratense* L. Plant Physiol. **37**, 643—649 (1962).
— Factors controlling the synthesis of natural and induced lignins in *Phleum* and *Elodea*. Plant Physiol. **40**, 844—851 (1965).
STONE, J. E.: Studies of lignin biosynthesis using isotopic carbon. I. Long-term experiment with $^{14}CO_2$. Can. J. Chem. **31**, 207—213 (1953).
SUHADOLNIK, R. J., and J. ZULALIAN: Biosynthesis of the amaryllidaceae alkaloids. Part IV. The incorporation of cinnamic, *p*-coumaric and caffeic acid into haemanthamine and lycorine. Proc. Chem. Soc. **1963**, 216.
SWAIN, T.: The biosynthesis of polyphenols. In: Wood extractives, pp. 277—313. Edited by HILLIS, W. E. New York: Academic Press 1962.
TOWERS, G. H. N.: Comparative chemistry and taxonomy of plants: The separation and estimation of phenolic aldehydes from the alkaline nitrobenzene oxidation mixtures of plant materials. M.Sc. Thesis, McGill University, Montreal, Canada, 1951.
—, and R. D. GIBBS: Lignin chemistry and the taxonomy of higher plants. Nature **172**, 25—26 (1953).
UNDERHILL, E. W., J. E. WATKIN, and A. C. NEISH: Biosynthesis of quercetin in buckwheat. I. Can. J. Biochem. and Physiol. **35**, 219—228 (1957).

WATKIN, J. E., and A. C. NEISH: Biosynthesis of quercetin in buckwheat. Part III. Can. J. Biochem. and Physiol. **38**, 559—567 (1960).

—, E. W. UNDERHILL, and A. C. NEISH: Biosynthesis of quercetin in buckwheat. Part II. Can. J. Biochem. and Physiol. **35**, 229—237 (1957).

WEINSTEIN, L. H., C. A. PORTER, and H. J. LAURENCOT: (1) Evidence for the conversion of quinic acid to shikimic acid in roses. Nature **183**, 326 (1959).

— —, and H. J. LAURENCOT, Jr.: (2) Quinic acid as a precursor in aromatic biosynthesis in the Rose. Contribs. Boyce Thompson Inst. **20**, 121—134 (1959).

— — — Role of quinic acid in aromatic biosynthesis in higher plants. Contribs. Boyce Thompson Inst. **21**, 201—214 (1961).

— —, and H. J. LAURENCOT: Role of the shikimic acid pathway in the formation of tryptophan in higher plants: Evidence for an alternative pathway in the bean. Nature **194**, 205—206 (1962).

WIESNER, J.: Das Verhalten des Phloroglucins und einiger verwandter Körper zur verholzten Zellmembran. Sitzber. Akad. Wiss. Wien Abt. I **77**, 60—66 (1878).

WRIGHT, D., S. A. BROWN, and A. C. NEISH: Studies of lignin biosynthesis using isotopic carbon. VI. Formation of the side chain of the phenylpropane monomer. Can. J. Biochem. and Physiol. **36**, 1037—1045 (1958).

YOUNG, M. R., and A. C. NEISH: Properties of ammonia-lyases deaminating phenylalanine and related compounds in *Triticum aestivum* and *Pteridium aquilinum*. Phytochemistry **5**, 1121—1132 (1966).

—, G. H. N. TOWERS, and A. C. NEISH: Taxonomic distribution of ammonia-lyases for L-phenylalanine and L-tyrosine in relation to lignification. Can. J. Botany **44**, 341—349 (1966).

ZENK, M. H.: Zur Frage der Biosynthese von Gallussäure. Z. Naturforsch. **19b**, 83—84 (1964).

—, u. G. MÜLLER: Biosynthese von *p*-Hydroxybenzoesäure und anderer Benzoesäuren in höheren Pflanzen. Z. Naturforsch. **19b**, 398—405 (1964).

ZULALIAN, J., and R. J. SUHADOLNIK: Biosynthesis of the amaryllidaceae alkaloids. V. Caffeic acid and protocatechuic aldehyde as C_6—C_1 precursors of haemanthamine and lycorine. Proc. Chem. Soc. **1964**, 422.

Karl Freudenberg

The Constitution and Biosynthesis of Lignin

Dedicated to the Memory of Bror Holmberg (1881—1966)

Table of Contents

Part I

A. The Beginning . . . 47
B. Lignin Preparations and Their Isolation . . . 50
C. Lignin Derivatives and Their Preparation . . . 53
D. The Aromatic Nature of Lignin . . . 55
E. Other Observations . . . 60
1. Liberation of Formaldehyde; Search for C-Methyl . . . 60
2. Oxidation to Vanillin and Allied Materials . . . 61
3. Other Oxidation Products . . . 62
4. Hydrogenation . . . 62
5. Lignin and Alcohols . . . 63
F. The Elemental Analysis of Lignin and the Calculation of Its Composition . . . 64
1. Introductory Remarks . . . 64
2. Expression of Lignin Analyses . . . 65
3. Recalculation of Analyses for Acetyllignin . . . 66
4. Recalculation of Analyses for Methyllignin . . . 67
5. Recalculation of Lignothioglycolic Acid . . . 68
G. Analytical Data on Lignin . . . 69
1. Elemental Composition . . . 69
2. Hydroxyl Estimation . . . 70
3. Carbonyl Groups . . . 72
4. Ether Oxygen and Oxygen Balance . . . 72
H. Early Approaches to the Constitution of Lignin . . . 74

Part II

A. Degradation of Lignin to Methoxybenzenecarboxylic Acids and Other Products . 78
1. Compounds of the Catechol (Veratrole) Series . . . 78
2. Compounds of the Anisole Series . . . 80
3. Compounds of the Trimethoxybenzene Series . . . 80
4. Other Oxidation Products . . . 80
B. The Dehydrogenation of Coniferyl Alcohol . . . 82
1. Introductory Remarks . . . 82
2. Monolignols . . . 85
3. Dilignols . . . 86
4. Trilignols . . . 91
5. Higher Oligolignols . . . 91
C. Linkage of Lignin with Carbohydrates . . . 92
D. Quinone Methides: Benzyl Aryl Ethers in Lignin; Hydrolysis Products . . . 93
E. Biochemical and Tracer Experiments . . . 97
1. Biochemical Experiments and Other Observations . . . 97
2. Tracer Experiments . . . 99
F. Schematic Model of the Constitution of Spruce Lignin . . . 102
G. Appraisal of the Schematic Formula for Spruce Lignin . . . 105
H. Other Proposals for Formulae . . . 108
I. Beech Lignin, Other Kinds of Lignin and the Concept of Lignin; Lignite and Humic Acid . . . 110
1. Beech Lignin and Other Kinds of Lignin . . . 110
2. The Concept of Lignin . . . 114
3. Fossilized Wood (Lignite) . . . 115
4. Humic Substances . . . 115
K. Concluding Remark . . . 116
L. References . . . 116

Part I

A. The Beginning

Over the past fifty years the chemistry of lignin has proliferated from uncertain beginnings to a broad field of science. It has been my good fortune, after some initial groping, to participate in the climactic phase of this development. In response to repeated requests I decided to retrace the diverse and devious pathways followed in the last five decades.

It is mainly the situations that my associates and I encountered on this long route that are described; many results obtained by other workers must remain unmentioned. I am referring to recent articles on some aspects of the work reported here: K. Freudenberg* (1962, 1962a, 1964a, 1965, 1966) and J. M. Harkin (1966, 1967).

The development of lignin chemistry was closely connected with the question of whether or not lignin is an aromatic substance. I was convinced of the first alternative, from its beginnings to the definitive conclusion that it belongs to the widespread natural group of phenylpropane derivatives. When this question was settled, the biochemistry of lignin divided itself into two problems:

1. How are the phenylpropane precursors formed in nature; and
2. How are they transformed into lignin?

The first problem is dealt with by A. C. Neish (1968) in the preceding paper, whereas my task is to describe the path of research leading to the incorporation of lignin into the phenylpropanoids and to show how lignin is formed from them.

My first encounter with lignin came as a matter of chance. In February, 1916, during my military service in World War I, I received an order to report to Berlin. My former mentor, Emil Fischer, had reclaimed me for the following reason: Chromium salts and vegetable tannins had become scarce in Germany and substitutes for them were being sought. In order to determine whether spent sulfite liquors could be used either as an expander for other tanning agents or to accelerate their effect, an improvised research program on sulfite liquors was started.

I had some experience in the chemistry of natural tannins, for I had worked under Emil Fischer on the structures of gallotannins, but I had only scant experience in the technological process involved in tanning. For this reason the tanning expert, Professor E. Stiasny, was also withdrawn from the Austro-Hungarian army to supplement our team. We worked together in Fischer's institute and received frequent visits from the master himself. I began to work on the fractionation of industrial lignosulfonates in order to find out if fractions with improved tanning

* Abbreviation in the following: Fr.

I acknowledge gratefully the help of Dr. J. M. Harkin who contributed to the manuscript by discussions and translation.

properties could be obtained. Promising preliminary results were obtained, but after only 2 months STIASNY and I were ordered back to our units. Some of the natural products with which I had dealt before the War, e.g. phlobaphenes and tannins, did not seem very remote in their properties from lignin itself. From that time on I was convinced that lignin belongs to the phenols.

After the War I began working with catechin. In addition to the gallotannins, which were amorphous and which had exceptionally high molecular weights for the organic substances known at that time, I encountered high molecular-weight tannin-like, and finally even insoluble condensation products of catechin. Toward the end of 1921 I reverted to lignosulfonic acids and in 1922 completed a series of experiments. After the preparation of di-1,2:5,6-*O*-isopropylidene-3-*O*-*p*-tolylsulfonyl-D-glucofuranose (1921), I had recognized the unusually high stability of some toluenesulfonic esters (FR. and IVERS, 1922). In the meantime, in the work on natural tannins, I had also learned that substances with tannin groups, in the crystalline state, are highly insoluble in water. The crystalline state is often difficult or impossible to achieve, but when, as is ordinarily the case, the natural tannins occur in mixtures or in the hydrated state, they readily dissolve in water to give supersaturated solutions (FR. 1920, p. 3).

If a few hydrophobic groups are introduced into materials which tend to have tanning properties so that their potential solubility in the crystalline state is reduced, amorphous, water-soluble mixtures with improved tanning properties can be obtained. For example, monoactyl catechin gives a more copious precipitation with gelatin solution than catechin does (FR., BÖHME and PURRMANN, 1922). With this consideration in mind, lignosulfonates were partially esterified with *p*-toluenesulfonyl chloride in alkaline medium, and the products were salted out. They were readily soluble in water and had better tanning ability than unmodified lignosulfonates. These esterified products readily precipitated gelatin from dilute solutions and even precipitated molybdic acid from its solution in nitric acid, although lignosulfonate could not. The experiments that led to these results were carried out under my direction in the Melanolwerke in Freiburg, Germany. Unexpectedly, our findings were recorded in the patents of M. MELAMID (1926) and were communicated by MELAMID (1923) to the Hugo Stinnes Riebeck Montan- und Ölwerke AG. (1926) and to OSKAR BEYER who published a survey of the results (1922, 1923).

I also received another stimulus from a different direction, which was for me at the same time an introduction into the field of polymeric natural compounds. This occurred in connection with cellulose.

EMIL FISCHER had died in 1919. He had established the systematic family tree of the monosaccharides and had recognized these to be bifunctional compounds — as they were called later — which could intercombine by forming glycosidic linkages to yield di- and trisaccharides which possessed the same reactive groups (cf. FR., 1966a, 1967). The only degradation product of cellulose known then, apart from glucose, was cellobiose. It was already reported in the literature that yields of 37 to 43% of cellobiose could be procured from cellulose (OST, 1913; MADSEN, 1917). I could find no way of increasing the yield of cellobiose (FR., 1921). The reaction that was used to degrade the cellulose was its acetolysis, and the cellobiose was obtained in the form of its crystalline octa-acetate. We were able to show that, during the acetolysis, about 20% more of the cellobiose derivative must be split to yield 40% of cristalline octa-O-acetylcellobiose hence, the total amount of cellobiose formed during the reaction must have been a little more than 60%, the loss of 20% being due to unavoidable degradations during the acetolysis. Using another method, KARRER and WIDMER (1921), independently, found the same loss of cellobiose during its isolation; they did not draw further conclusions concerning the constitution of cellulose.

Working on the assumption that in a chain of one hundred units there are 99 glucosidic linkages that can all be attacked and split at an equal rate, we were able to carry out a statistical calculation revealing that not more than 67% of the units can pass through the stage of cellobiose. This is based on the fact that, on an average, an equal amount of degradation products with odd and even numbers of glucose units is obtained. Further calculation revealed that in a *homogeneous* system the content of cellobiose would rise to a maximum of 33% and then fall off to 0%. (FR., 1921, 1967). In practice, however, during the acetolysis, some of the octa-*O*-acetylcellobiose precipitates out because of its low solubility in the medium. The system is therefore not entirely homogeneous. The yield of product actually obtained must therefore lie between 33 and 67%. A little more than 40% can in fact be found whereas 20% is lost during the preparation. Thus, the experimental results agree very satisfactorily with the concept of a chain of glucose residues, each of which is linked to the next by one and the same steric and glucosidic pattern (FR., 1921). Furthermore, the nature of the interunit bond must be the same as that in cellobiose itself.

By elaborating the experimental consequences of this conception and combining it with the results of the British school, I was able to publish the first cellulose formula in 1928 (FR., 1928, 1967).

Impressed by the orderliness and simplicity that I had encountered in the molecular structure of cellulose, I set myself to enquire if the same sort of situation might prevail in other polymeric natural materials as well. I turned my attention to starch (FR., 1933, 1963, 1965a, 1967), which from the outset commanded part of my activities in addition to cellulose. I recalled my short association with lignin, which invariably occurs together with cellulose in nature and which, when one considers the manifold species in which it is present, is surely the most abundant organic natural material after cellulose. Had it not been for the confidence in an orderly constitution of polymers that I had received from my early work on cellulose, I should never have risked attacking the problem of lignin, for not even the haziest notions about the nature of polymeric molecules were developed at that time.

In those early days of polymer chemistry the question was: Is lignin a refuse product of nature? Is it like peat or leaf-mould, which are the remains of a vast number of different plants or plant-leaves? Or is it a kind of a chemical individual, which like cellulose has an intelligible architectural structure that can be discerned by chemical scrutiny? An important indication of an orderly structural principle in lignin is its methoxyl content. The methoxyl content of lignin from conifers is fairly constant at 14 to 15% (UNGAR 1916). Moreover, the fact that lignin arises under physiological conditions in living plant cells tends to imply that it should have an ordered and not a fortuitous constitution.

It seemed worthwhile to examine whether this rather uncertain evidence could be supplemented. I realized that it would be a long time before an answer to these questions would be obtained, and I foresaw that the return on even intensive efforts would at first be meagre. My decision to project a long-term program in this work was abetted in 1922 by fortunate circumstances, which afforded me permanent and favorable working conditions.

For almost 30 years the progress we made on the lignin problem was depressingly slow. At the start there were hardly any clues as to how we should even begin to approach the problem. As time progressed, however, one little success added to the next, and could be combined with the results from other laboratories. Nonetheless, we had to wait until 1952 (Fr. and Hübner, 1952) to achieve the first real breakthrough; that has brought us, within the past 15 years, to a substantial knowledge of the constitution of lignin and led to the design of a formula scheme for the material that appears to come close to the truth.

Such a scientific undertaking can only mature in the surroundings of other allied projects. The polysaccharides have already been mentioned. Throughout the entire period of our lignin research, the work on catechins and their spontaneous condensation, which later led to studies of natural condensed proanthocyanidins (Fr. and Weinges, 1962, 1962 a, 1965), was continued. The same applies to our investigations of sugars, proteins and stereochemistry (Fr., 1933 a, 1965 a). Ideas and experimental experience flowed over from these fields of research to stimulate the work on lignin. The observations made in these other sectors also helped us to overcome the weariness and setbacks in the first decades of our lignin work. It was only after 1950 that lignin became my main field of research.

At the outset, just after the first World War, the most important starting point reached was that: Emil Fischer had indeed recognized that the principle of the interlinking of bifunctional molecular residues (monosaccharides, amino acids, hydroxybenzenecarboxylic acids) gave materials which he regarded as possessing high molecular weights (Fr., 1966 a). But the extension of his ideas to condensed (i.e. nonhydrolysable) systems made only slow progress. Moreover, lignin was a most unsuitable object with which to attempt to gain insight into the principles of molecular growth by polycondensation, for although each unit evolves from the same source, in the finished product only few of the units are alike. Even today lignin still differs from any other natural high polymer because of the stepwise nature of its growth by agglomeration and the diversity of its bonding principles.

B. Lignin Preparations and Their Isolation

It was recognized at a very early stage in the history of lignin research that it differed from cellulose and the other saccharide components of wood. When Payen (1838, cf. p. 56 and Adler 1966), treated different kinds of wood with nitric acid, he found in all samples a suhstance which had the composition of starch. He called it cellulose. Benedikt and Bamberger (1890) discovered the methoxyl content of wood and ascribed it to another constituent of the wood, lignin, although lignin could not be isolated as such at that time. Klason (1908, 1911, 1911 a) later developed the method of liberating the lignin from wood with strong sulfuric acid for purposes of quantitative assay; his preparation was, however, unsuitable for chemical investigations. This situation was improved in 1913 when WILLSTÄTTER and ZECHMEISTER (1913) dissolved out the polysaccharide components of spruce wood with cold 40% hydrochloric acid and found the residual lignin to be "purer than that obtained by the action of sulfuric acid on wood". Afterwards it was called hydrochloric acid lignin.

A less aggressive reagent was found in a 3:1 vol/vol mixture of 36% hydrochloric acid and 80% phosphoric acid (URBAN, 1926, 1926 a). Alternate boiling of wood with 2% sulfuric acid and subsequent treatment with ammoniacal copper oxide proved to be even milder (FR., HARDER and MARKERT, 1928; FR., ZOCHER and DÜRR, 1929). The "cuproxam lignin" isolated by extraction of the wood carbohydrates in this manner differed from the "acid lignins" in having a pale color. Other efforts to release lignin from wood include the dissolution of the polysaccharides using liquefied hydrogen fluoride (FREDENHAGEN and CADENBACH, 1933; WIECHERT, 1940). The extraction of lignin preparations with the aid of alcohols and mineral acid catalysts are not referred to here because the products have invariably taken up both alkyl groups and inorganic anions and are altered by condensation reactions during the extraction process.

The results are no better when hot dioxan and mineral acid are used (ENGEL and WEDEKIND, 1932). If the dioxan is not carefully purified beforehand to remove esters and acetals, condensations occur, as in the case of the alcohols above. The mineral acid also causes condensation reactions within the lignin itself. Extraction of the wood at room temperature with pure dioxan and hydrochloric acid is slightly superior (STUMPF and FR., 1950); no condensation reactions between lignin and dioxan occur, as was shown by using radioactive dioxan for the extraction (STUMPF, WEYGAND and GROSSKINSKI, 1953); but the product contains a few percent of chlorine. All of these methods, except perhaps the last, lead to drastic inter- and intramolecular condensations of the lignin. Even when no extraneous materials are condensed with the lignin, such changes can nevertheless be surmised to have occurred intramolecularily because of the loss of thermoplasticity.

Another approach to the isolation of lignin was introduced by SCHÜTZ and KNACKSTEDT (1942), i.e. heating wood in acetic acid in the presence of magnesium chloride. The lignin is dissolved and separated from the cellulose. However, it has an acetyl content; this can be removed by subsequent saponification with alkali in the cold in the absence of air (FR. and PLANKENHORN, 1942). The preparation obtained in this way is thermoplastic and free from any condensed acetic acid, as was later shown by using radioactive acetic acid (FR. and WERNER FUCHS, 1954). However, it has not yet been shown whether or not the benzyl aryl ethers present in lignin remain unattacked and whether the primary alcoholic groups, which tend to lose formaldehyde, remain intact in any of the lignin isolation procedures which involve acids. Residues of carbohydrates may also be present in some of the products. The acetic acid lignins probably deserve greater attention than they have received to date.

With the aim of securing intact lignin without chemical operations, BRAUNS (1939, 1952, BRAUNS and BRAUNS 1960) extracted degummed wood with neutral organic solvents. In order to avoid alcohols we prefer to percolate the finely powdered wood exhaustively with pure acetone containing water (9:1 v/v) at room temperature. No further material can be dissolved out of the wood extracted in this way under the conditions selected by BRAUNS. The acetone extracts from the wood of the European spruce *Picea excelsa* contain 0.3% (calculated from the wood) of the lignan hydroxymatairesinol and further 0.3% of a mixture of other lignans and of various oligolignols (FR. and KNOF, 1957; HARKIN, 1966) [lignols are the dehydrogenative condensation products of *p*-hydroxycinnamyl alcohols at any stage of condensation (FR., 1963 a)].

The low molecular-weight impurities in the soluble or "native" lignin can be dissolved out with cold ethyl acetate (NIMZ, 1963), and the remaining residue of "soluble lignin" is then only 0.2 to 0.4% of the original amount of spruce wood. This material is soluble in acetone/water (9:1 v/v) at 20 °C; it does not move on paper chromatograms and migrates as a single band on paper electrophoresis. When dried above 50 °C or kept for months, it becomes partially insoluble in acetone/water: this may be due to the formation of hydrogen bonds. It is very similar to the spruce milled-wood lignin prepared by the method of BJÖRKMAN described below, but contains more phenolic hydroxyl groups and cannot therefore be regarded as a typical representative of the total lignin of the plant. The same also applies to the "enzymatically liberated lignin" of SCHUBERT and NORD (1950): this preparation is not liberated from the other components of the wood by *isolated* enzymes but is the material extractable from the residue remaining after digestion of the wood by living microorganisms, mainly wood-rotting fungi of the brown rot type. Since NORD found his preparation to be identical with soluble lignin, it is probably not typical of the unchanged lignin in the wood.

BROWN et al. (1967) also used, for the degradation of wood, living organisms instead of isolated enzymes. Their consideration regarding the molecular weight of lignin preparations is therefore not conclusive.

It seems no longer necessary to use names such as "native-, pseudo-, protolignin" or "hemilignin" etc. Two natural kinds of lignin are known so far. The main product is the insoluble lignin in wood; it has not yet been isolated without alteration. It is at least in part — grafted on polysaccharides; another part may be insoluble because of the large size of its molecule. This then is "lignin"; it needs no other name. The other kind, the "soluble lignin", is a very small fraction (in spruce wood about 1% of the lignin); it is contained in F. E. BRAUNS' preparations and differs from the lignin chemically and by its lower molecular weight, its solubility and its higher content of phenolic hydroxyl. Besides, there exists artificial lignin.

An unobjectionable lignin preparation for scientific investigations was first prepared by BJÖRKMAN (1954, 1956, 1957); he called it "milled wood lignin" (MWL) because it is extracted with organic solvents from the wood after mechanical degradation, and has not been subjected to any chemical processing. A standardized method for working up the milled wood has been elaborated (HARKIN, 1966/67).

Wood meal prepared by dry grinding is preextracted with acetone/water (9:1 v/v) and after drying under reduced pressure, finely milled following BJÖRKMAN in suspension with a liquid that does not swell the wood fibres, e.g. toluene. The toluene is then removed by filtration. The low-molecular-weight material is then extracted with cold ethyl acetate, and the main product dissolved by repeated extraction with dioxane/water (9:1 v/v). This solution is then brought to a concentration of 0.3% of the crude product. The fractions contaminated with carbohydrate are now precipitated by dropwise addition of 80 ccm benzene to 1 l of the dioxane/water solution and a two-gram portion of aluminium oxide (neutral, Woelm Co.) is mixed with the precipitate to facilitate filtration. After filtration the solution is concentrated to a small volume under reduced pressure and then freeze-dried. The final product contains less than 0.2% of carbohydrates. From 150 g of dry wood, 15 g of raw product and 10 g of carbohydrate-free MW lignin are obtained. This is 25% of the lignin present in the wood. Another way (for analyses only) to remove the carbohydrates is by treatment with 70% sulfuric acid (KLASON 1908; cf. p. 113).

The spruce milled-wood lignin obtained in this way is a pale yellow or buff colored powder. It is characteristic of this lignin that it does not migrate on paper chromatograms with the solvent mixtures used for chromatographing oligolignols (FR. and LEHMANN, 1960, 1963) as is the case when the molecular weight of the material exceeds about 8000. The upper limit of molecular weight is predetermined by the solubility of the MW lignin in aqueous dioxane or acetone. The molecular weight of the MWL obtained in this way lies between 8000 and 11000. The mean molecular weight of the lignin in wood is assumed to be higher. Milled-wood lignin is therefore a mixture of fragments of the lignin as it occurs in the plant. It is nevertheless suitable for chemical and analytical studies, for its degree of polymerisation lies above 40, so that the positions of fracture are of only minor significance.

There have been numerous other attempts to isolate lignin or lignin derivatives from wood. These are described in the monographs on lignin chemistry by BRAUNS and BRAUNS (1952, 1960). Derivatives having significance for the investigation of lignin as a natural substance are mentioned in the next chapter.

C. Lignin Derivatives and Their Preparation

Only those conversion products of lignin that are of importance for a purely scientific investigation will be discussed here.

Sulfur containing products: On heating with sodium hydrogen sulfite or other acidic salts of sulfurous acid, lignin is separated from other components of wood and rendered soluble in water. Lignin preparations from industrial spent sulfite wastes are not suitable for chemical studies of lignin because: 1. the wood used in their preparation is not always specially selected nor transformed into sawdust and extracted; 2. the conditions used for digestion are adjusted to effect the fastest throughput in the pulping plant and disregard any alterations that may occur in the lignin. It is not yet known whether during the sulfite process condensations occur in addition to the degradation reactions.

A mild sulfite pulping method requiring a temperature of only 70 °C was developed (FR., LAUTSCH and PIAZOLO, 1944). This reaction was run for several weeks and gave rise to fractions with gradually increasing sulfur content. The reason for such an increase may be that aggregates of higher molecular size need relatively more SO_3H groups to become soluble than do smaller ones.

HÄGGLUND (1925, 1926) found that neutral sulfite reacts with lignin at 100 °C but does not cause its dissolution out of the wood fiber. The weakly sulfonated lignin produced under these conditions must be released from the wood by subsequent hydrolysis. A method evolved by HARTLER, RÖNSTRÖM and STOCKMAN (1961) is useful for special requirements. Aqueous sulfur dioxide alone is capable of releasing a major part of the lignin from wood at 80 °C. Both milled-wood lignin and the artificial biosynthetic lignins to be described later dissolve under these conditions if dioxane is added to aid dispersion (FR., HARKIN and WERNER, 1964); this modification has been of some use for studying special problems. If inorganic salts are used, the cations can be removed with ion exchangers. Solutions of lignosulfonic acid must not be made too concentrated, otherwise the strong sulfonic acid groupings cause alterations of the materials even when freeze-drying is applied. It is best to neutralize the sulfonic acids with ammonia and freeze-dry the products (FR., HARKIN, WERNER 1964). This gives rise to ammonium lignosulfonates which can be kept indefinitely in the dry state without change. So far, investigations of lignosulfonic acids have not provided much information about the structure of lignin. However, clarification of their mode of formation was an important step in lignin chemistry. This subject is discussed below.

The reaction of lignin in wood with sodium hydrogen sulfide, hydrogen sulfide or thiols also afforded important technical products and valuable insight into the processes occurring during kraft or sulfate pulping (ENKVIST and LINDFORS, 1966), but the use of these reagents for research on the constitution of lignin is still at an elementary stage.

An important long-established reaction of lignin is that with thioglycolic acid, introduced by HOLMBERG (1930). In order to prepare the thioglycolic acid derivative of lignin, HOLMBERG allowed a solution of this acid in hot hydrochloric acid to react with wood meal. It was later found that the same reaction occurs rapidly at 20 °C if an excess of anhydrous thioglycolic acid acts on the wood powder in the presence of a trace of boron trifluoride etherate (FR., SEIB and DALL, 1959). The thioglycolic acid reacts with the benzyl alcohols and their ethers and blocks them from further reactions. The lignin is thus removed from the carbohydrates, with which it is linked via benzyl ether groupings. In addition, esters are formed between the ligno-thioglycolic acid and the alcoholic groups in the lignin or carbohydrates. These are split by mild alkaline hydrolysis, and the lignothioglycolic acid is then precipitated from the solution with acid. This reaction provides a method for characterizing lignins. Lignothioglycolic acids are probably closer in structure to the original lignin than any other lignin preparation except milled-wood lignin. In contrast to the MWL process, lignothioglycolic acid represents the total lignin content of the wood. Thioglycolic acid is therefore a most useful reagent for assaying the elemental composition of lignins. The formation of a lignothioglycolic acid can even be taken as a criterion for a genuine lignin; substances that do not give such a derivative cannot be classified as lignin. This point is developed on p. 64, 68 and 115.

Methyl lignin: Finely powdered wood is percolated at room temperature with acetone/water (9:1 v/v) and then methylated, first with diazomethane in dioxan and then with alkali and a large excess of dimethyl sulfate below 20 °C (FR. and KRAFT, 1950). As a rule, it is advantageous to methylate with dimethylsulfate at 15° (URBAN 1926, 1926a) or even at 0° as suggested by HARKIN (1966/67).

The methylated wood is filtered off from the neutral solution. The material is washed and subjected to the same treatment repeatedly without intermittent drying. When no further increase in methoxyl content is observed, the product is dried at 20 °C and suspended in a large excess of 98% formic acid containing 1% acetyl chloride. After several hours at 20 °C, the methylated polysaccharides are largely degraded and become soluble in water. Sodium acetate is added to neutralize the hydrochloric acid released, the solution is concentrated to dryness in vacuo, and the residue stirred with water. The insoluble methylated lignin is filtered off, remethylated and again treated with formic acid plus acetyl chloride. This leads to a product that is almost completely soluble in chloroform.

During these operations, probably both the benzyl polysaccharide ether bonds and the benzyl aryl ether bonds within the lignin itself are hydrolysed or trans-etherified. If the benzyl moieties have not undergone condensation reactions — unfortunately this is not known for sure — this methyl lignin ought to be a good material for chemical research on lignin. So far little work has been done with it. Methyl lignin obtained from wood in this way is very similar to methylated milled-wood lignin and to methylated artificial lignin. Formic acid is not condensed into the lignin in the presence of hydrochloric acid; this has been proven using radioactive formic acid (FR. and WERNER FUCHS 1954).

D. The Aromatic Nature of Lignin

According to the international rules of nomenclature (IUPAC Rules, 1960), the carbons in the sidechain of the cinnamyl alcohols should be designated by α, β, and γ, starting from the free end of the hydroxypropenyl residue and ending next to the benzene ring. This nomenclature is adopted here, but it is at variance with that of other authors; they designate the terminal (hydroxylated) carbon as γ and that next to the benzene ring as α. In order to circumvent this divergence in nomenclature and in order to be able to indicate the relationship to the corresponding cinnamic acids and phenylalanine, one can speak of the "terminal, middle and ring-adjacent carbons". When the ring-adjacent carbon atom — or in the international nomenclature, the γ-carbon atom — bears a free or etherified hydroxyl group, the groupings are referred to in the following as benzyl alcohols and benzyl ethers.

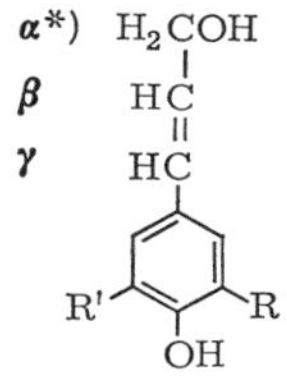

α*) H_2COH terminal
β HC middle
γ HC ring adjacent
R' R
OH

(1a) R', R = H
p-Coumaryl alcohol

(1b) R = OCH_3, R' = H
Coniferyl alcohol

(1c) R, R' = OCH_3
Sinapyl alcohol

*) international nomenclature

Now that it is known for certain that lignin is a derivative of the C_6 C_3 group — the phenylpropanoids — it seems worthwhile to retrace the evolution of this situation through the literature. Already during their elucidation of the glucoside coniferin TIEMANN and MENDELSOHN (1875) suspected some connection between this compound and lignin. They could not prove their assertions for they had no lignin preparation for purposes of comparison. Later, many authors studied spent sulfite liquors, and GRAFE (1904) found that a few percent of vanillin could be obtained from the lignin of this waste product by treating it with hot lime. KLASON (1897) found that coniferyl alcohol (*1 b*), the aglycon of coniferin, gave rise to a sulfonic acid, or rather a mixture of sulfonic acids under the conditions of a sulfite cook. This material seemed to be similar to lignosulfonates. He also investigated the aldehyde reactions of spent sulfite liquors, and in 1911 postulated two spruce lignins, which he surmised to be highmolecular-weight condensation products of coniferyl alcohol and a hydroxyconiferyl alcohol (KLASON, 1907, 1911 a). KLASON (1897, 1925) occasionally also visualized lignin as a trimer of coniferaldehyde. The first fairly correct analysis of spruce lignin seems to be given by KLASON (1908, see p 69). Today it may be regarded as a first orientation, but it confirmed him in his view that lignin is an oxidation product of coniferyl alcohol (see p. 75). His more detailed views were not based on accurate analyses or other quantitative proofs, but mainly on colour reactions and probably also on the general impressions he received during his work with lignosulfonic acids. He constantly maintained the opinion that lignin is a derivative of an oxidation product of coniferyl alcohol.

In 1911 ZECHMEISTER concluded his doctoral thesis under WILLSTÄTTER. During this work the dissolution of cellulose in 40 to 41% hydrochloric acid was discovered or rediscovered. It was found that during lignification the carbon content of the polysaccharide tissues increased from 44.5% to almost 50% in the mature wood. (Similar observations had been made by A. PAYEN in 1838.) The hydrogen content remained roughly constant at about 6%, but the oxygen content decreased and a methoxyl content developed. The color reactions of lignin were discussed in detail by ZECHMEISTER and model reactions with aromatic aldehydes were examined. ZECHMEISTER concluded that "the cellulose component is linked through oxygen bonds to the lignin component" and that the latter contains "aromatic rings and carbonyl".

In a later doctoral thesis carried out with WILLSTÄTTER, UNGAR (1916) found that carbohydrate-free isolated lignin prepared from sprucewood contained almost the entire methoxyl content of the wood. The methoxyl content of hydrochloric acid lignin from spruce was 15%. If wood was methylated with diazomethane and then degraded with cold hydrochloric acid, the methyl groups introduced were found to be distributed between its two main components, i.e. the lignin and the polysaccharides. Wood coupled with benzenediazonium sulfonic acid gives a colored product. UNGAR was led to the "assumption of pyrone or furan groupings in the lignin molecule", which suggested "the possibility of its formation from aliphatic materials". On the other hand, a few years later, WALTER FUCHS (1921) voiced the hitherto prevalently accepted opinion, as follows: "There are methoxyl groups in all lignin materials. Only a minute fraction of these are readily removable, in the main they are attached by a strong aromatic bond". Wherever evidence was available and opinions had been formed, an aromatic nature had been ascribed to lignin. The only contrary standpoint was assumed by UNGAR.

WILLSTÄTTER and KALB (1922) published a paper which subsequently had great repercussions. On hydrogenation of lignin with hydroiodic acid and phosphorus at 250 °C, they obtained a mixture of hydrocarbons of average composition $(CH_{1.6})_n$. Cellulose and other carbohydrates yielded similar mixtures. It was therefore concluded that "it can be assumed that five- and six-membered rings, being the most stable, will occur in the final products. As a result of this work, it can be concluded that the similarity in behavior between lignin and carbohydrates is compatible with a close constitutional connection between these materials and even strongly supports this view. Furan derivatives and perhaps also diolefins are probably intermediates".

These conclusions proved to be incorrect, but they found avid supporters. More than 25 years elapsed before this opinion lost all its defenders. The supporters of this theory included W. SCHRAUTH (1923); R. S. HILPERT (1936); HILPERT, LITTMANN and WIENBECK (1937), F. SCHÜTZ (1943); SCHÜTZ, SARTEN and MEYER (1948) and, temporarily, C. A. SANKEY and H. HIBBERT (1931). Originally it was believed that lignin existed in the wood as a carbohydrate-type compound; later it was supposed that this product was transformed into an aromatic artifact during its isolation. The hydrogenation method used by WILLSTÄTTER and KALB was so drastic that it was not permissible to draw such far reaching conclusions from it. The arguments presented by later authors in favor of this hypothesis were unfounded and did not result in any progress in lignin chemistry.

KÜRSCHNER (1925) found that vanillic acid could be sublimed out of lignin. It is, however, strongly embedded in resinous material and the yield of pure substance is therefore low. KÜRSCHNER placed great trust in the significance of his experiment and therefore favored the older theory that lignin was derived from coniferyl alcohol or its glucoside coniferin.

In his thesis carried out in my laboratory in 1924 to 1926, H. URBAN (1926, 1926 a) stated in connection with the analysis of his lignin preparation that "if there is a connection with coniferyl alcohol, it is certainly very complicated". URBAN's work was not influenced by Willstätter's theory and does not refer to it directly.

The analyses of both KLASON and URBAN will be discussed on p. 69, 70.

The hypothesis of an aromatic constitution for lignin was supported by the quantitative approach to the lignin problem and in particular by investigation of the content of phenolic hydroxyl groups in lignin. FR. and H. HESS (1926) had found that hydrazine acts in a very different way on aliphatic and aromatic *p*-toluene-sulfonic esters. When di-*O*-isopropylideneglucose *p*-toluenesulfonate or other aliphatic arylsulfonates are treated with hydrazine, the sulfonic acid is liberated and olefins or alkyl hydrazines are formed. Aryl *p*-toluenesulfonates prepared from phenols behave differently: here the phenol is regenerated with hydrazine and *p*-toluenesulfohydrazide is formed. The latter is then reduced by an excess of hot hydrazine to the hydrazine salt of *p*-toluenesulfinic acid. The *p*-toluene sulfinic acid had at first been assayed as such. Spruce lignin *p*-toluenesulfonate gave rise to 0.22 mole of *p*-toluenesulfinic acid per methoxyl group; this implies a content of about 0.24 phenolic hydroxyl groups per phenylpropanoid unit in spruce lignin, when calculated according to the latest concepts. However, it was later established that this method is inadequate and produces at the best only minimum values. Apparently some of the sulfinic acid reacts with the lignin in the system. In later experiments even less or no sulfinic acid at all was found until it was released by treatment of the reaction mixture with dibenzylideneacetone (FR. and WALCH, 1943; cf. KOHLER and REIMER, 1904). Diazomethane reacts with lignin in the following manner (FR. and HESS, 1926). During the first 2 days the increase in methoxyl content of URBAN's lignin (p. 51) indicates a phenolic group content in lignin of 0.28 per phenylpropanoid unit when calculated by the modern method (p. 67). During the next 3 days this increases to 0.32. It is now known (pp. 71, 73) that milled-wood lignin from spruce contains a little more than 0,3 phenolic hydroxyls per C_9 unit.

The investigation carried out with H. HESS was also unhampered by Willstätter's hypothesis. In this paper, as well as in our previous work (URBAN), attention was called to the high incidence of ether linkages in lignin. This important observation raises the question of the amount of phenolic oxygen that is involved in ether bonds.

In another paper published in the next year by FR. and HARDER (1927), the aromatic system of lignin was also discussed; it was reported that lignin liberates about 2% of formaldehyde on heating with mineral acid. The formaldehyde is produced only from the lignin component of wood, and was at first ascribed to the aromatic part of lignin with the assumption that piperonyl residues occurred in the lignin.

On fusion of spruce hydrochloric acid lignin with potassium hydroxide, a yield of 8 to 10% of pure protocatechuic acid was obtained. Eugenol gave a similar yield (FR., HARDER and MARKERT, 1928).

Although the results described above clearly revealed that there are aromatic residues involved in the lignin polymolecule, it still remained undecided whether this aromatic portion was only an accessory, quantitatively unimportant fraction of the basic material. To clarify this matter, the bromination of lignin was investigated (FR., BELZ and NIEMANN, 1929). In order to suppress the formation and effects of hypobromous acid, a solution of bromine in aqueous hydrobromic acid was used. The amount of bromine consumed was measured by titration. The consumption was large for the first 2 h, and then rose gradually during the next 48 h. The bromine content of the residual insoluble lignin and the loss of methoxyl groups were determined. The processes occurring are the following: The main reaction is a substitution:

$$\text{RHH} + \text{Br–Br} \longrightarrow \text{RH–Br} + \text{HBr} .$$

This is followed by a second slow substitution:

$$\text{RH–Br} + \text{Br–Br} \longrightarrow \text{RBr}_2 + \text{HBr} .$$

This simple scheme does not adequately explain the difference between the bromine consumed and that found in the lignin (1.1 equivalent per original methoxyl group), for the amount of bromine condensed into the lignin was less than half of that consumed. In other words, more hydrogen bromide is formed than expected from the amount of bromine that enters the lignin by substitution. This is undoubtedly due to a side-reaction which causes loss of one-quarter to one-third of the original methoxyl content of the lignin. This reaction competes at the start with the substitution reaction but rapidly comes to a standstill.

The loss of methoxyl probably leads at first to an ortho-quinonoid product with simultaneous formation of methanol and hydrogen bromide or methyl bromide. If the amount of hydrogen bromide or methyl bromide formed in this side-reaction is deducted from the total bromine consumption, the remainder is exactly double the amount of bromine bonded in the lignin. The polymer formed H^+ from coniferyl alcohol gives similar results; however, here all three values (bromine consumed, bromine bonded in the product, and loss of methoxyl) are one-and-a-half times as large. It was appreciated that this is due to the lack of substitution of any of the guaiacyl residues in the polymer of coniferyl alcohol; furthermore all the phenolic hydroxyl groups are free.

The mode of action of hydroiodic acid on lignin characterizes its methoxyl content as being of aromatic origin (FR., BELZ and NIEMANN, 1929). It was therefore concluded that the methoxyl groups in a lignin are of the type shown in (*2*).

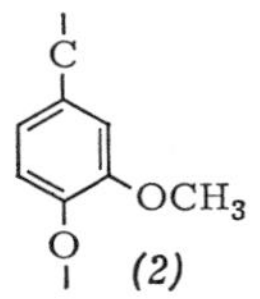

C

OCH_3

O

(2)

Lignin reacts with nitrogen dioxide in the same fashion as with bromine, i.e. mainly by substitution, to some extent by oxidation, causing a partial loss of methoxyl content, but not by addition (FR. and DÜRR, 1930). The results of such experiments were interpreted on the basis of guaiacylpropane derivatives with etherified and, to a smaller extent, free phenolic groups.

The largely aromatic nature of lignin is now firmly established. Numerous substitution reactions in the benzene rings in lignin have since been observed, e.g. mercuration with mercuric acetate, coupling with diazonium compounds, and a stoichiometric nitration.

On boiling methyl lignin with alcoholic mercuric acetate (FR. et al, 1931; FR. and MÜLLER, 1938 a), $HgOCOCH_3$ is introduced; this can be replaced quantitatively by iodine. The mercury content of the products is 43%. If one mercuric acetate group enters the lignin (p. 67) for each methylated unit with 30% methoxyl content, a maximum of 44% mercury would be expected in the product. The iodide content was raised to 36.5%; here 39% is the value to be expected, with one iodine atom for every methylated unit. The rate of reaction of the iodine in this product with sodium methoxide was compared with that of iodoveratric acid. The rates were equivalent.

The substitution reaction of diazobenzenesulfonic acid with lignin was examined by KÜSTER and DAUR (1930). It confirms the aromatic character of lignin. FR. and E. BRAUN (1931) used the salt of the coupling product of this reaction for a spreading experiment with lignin. The thickness of the molecular layer was shown to be 20 Å units. Recently NIKITIN and KROSHILOVA (1965) reinvestigated azo compounds of lignin.

Although most investigators of lignin no longer doubted its aromatic nature, attacks on this belief did not cease even after 1943 (SCHÜTZ, SARTEN and MEYER, 1948). One argument of these opponents was the lack of well defined nitro compounds of lignin. In practice, the nitration of lignin with nitric acid leads to a series of oxidation reactions and not to a definite nitro derivative. This is because of the phenolic groups in lignin and the introduction of new phenolic and quinonoid groupings by nitrous gases and air. For this reason, acetylated lignin was used, and the nitration was carried out with dinitrogen pentoxide in a mixture with chloroform at —20 °C. In this way, the development of nitrous gases was avoided (FR., LAUTSCH and PIAZOLO, 1943). The reaction ceases after the uptake of 0.9 nitro group per initial methoxyl group in the lignin. Here, and in other papers, the arguments for the aromatic nature of lignin (FR., SOHNS and JANSON, 1935; FR., 1939, 1947, 1948) were summarized. The carbon and oxygen balance of wood and its polysaccharides and lignin was presented, and once more the inapplicability of a cellulose anhydride which was supposed to form cellulose on the one side and lignin on the other was stressed. One argument supporting the opinion that lignin is formed only during its isolation was that although part of the lignin, particularly of beechwood, can be solubilized together with carbohydrates in strong mineral acid (HILPERT and HELLWAGE, 1935), or in water (SCHÜTZ, 1943; SCHÜTZ, SARTEN and MEYER, 1948), it precipitates shortly afterwards. Presumably the lignin portion of the soluble material precipitates when hydrolysis of the saccharide bonds, coupled with partial intra- and intermolecular condensations, gives rise to an increase in the molecular dimensions. These observations were explained in 1935 (FR., SOHNS and JANSON, 1935; FR., 1939) by arguments that are still valid today.

In the meantime physical methods were introduced. As early as 1920 HERZOG and JANCKE showed that with wood and jute the same X-ray diagram is produced as with cotton and ramie cellulose. Cellulose, therefore, is preformed as such in wood. Consequently, the carbon-richer component of wood, i.e. lignin, is likewise preformed. This postulate was generally recognized only after decades.

1927 HERZOG and HILLMER observed the similarity between the ultraviolet absorption spectra of spent sulfite liquors and those of coniferin and isoeugenol. They also found similarities between lignin itself and derivatives of coniferyl alcohol. In 1929 FR., ZOCHER, and DÜRR (1929) found that the refractive index (1.61) of spruce lignin, either as it occurred in the wood or even when isolated, is closely similar to that of iodobenzene, vanillin, guaiacol, or eugenol. Spruce lignin is therefore an aromatic substance while still in the wood. The same conclusion was reached by LANGE (1944, 1945) when he measured the ultraviolet absorption of lignin directly in wood.

From about 1930 onward, year after year, the arguments for the aromatic nature of lignin were augmented by the studies on the yield of vanillin, and by the work of H. ERDTMAN (1933, 1933a), B. HOLMBERG (1934—42), E. ADLER (1948), and many others. This shall be referred to in the following chapters.

E. Other Observations

1. Liberation of Formaldehyde; Search for C-Methyl

An early observation in lignin chemistry was that distillation of hydrochloric acid lignin with strong mineral acids by the method of TOLLENS gave a distillate which yielded a precipitate with phloroglucinol. It was originally assumed that this was due to pentosans. Later it was shown that it was not furfural but formaldehyde which caused this precipitate (FR. and HARDER, 1927; FR., HARDER and MARKERT, 1928). It was established that only about 2 to 3% formaldehyde was formed based on the lignin content (FR., 1928 a). Considering its low molecular weight, this amount is remarkably large.

The highest yields of formaldehyde are obtained by distillation from 28% sulfuric acid, according to SARKAR (1934). Beechwood lignin also yields formaldehyde, albeit in lower yield (FR. and MÜLLER, 1938).

It was long assumed that the formaldehyde originates from methylenedioxy residues of piperonyl groups, which were therefore supposed to occur in lignin. However, the fact that no piperonylic acid was encountered on oxidation of lignin gave rise to skepticism in this matter. It was found in 1938 that cinnamyl alcohol liberates formaldehyde under the same conditions as lignin (FR. et al., 1938).

The three-carbon side chain was therefore taken into consideration as the potential source of the aldehyde. Dicinnamyl ether and, to a minor extent, even coniferin also release formaldehyde with acids. Nevertheless, the probality that the aldehyde came from methylenedioxy groups was given additional support by the finding that both piperonylic acid and lignin gave rise to acridan with aniline and hydrochloric acid, whereas cinnamyl alcohol, dicinnamyl ether and coniferin did not (FR. et al.,

1939). It was not until 1943 that it became clear from work on lignin models, e.g. 1-guaiacyl-1-oxopropan-3-ol, that the formaldehyde is produced from the terminal primary alcoholic group of the side chain (FR., 1943). The question was finally resolved when it was shown (FR. and PLANKENHORN, 1947) that numerous model substances such as benzyl alcohol, dibenzyl ether and phenylpropanones of the above type all release formaldehyde under the same conditions as lignin, although various aromatic methylenedioxy compounds behave differently from lignin. Experiments carried out much later with a biosynthetic lignin made from coniferyl alcohol with a radioactive label in the terminal position of the side chain ([α-^{14}C] coniferyl alcohol) gave rise to radioactive formaldehyde (FR. and BITTNER, 1953).

The C-methyl content of lignin was observed by oxidation with hot chromic acid and distillation of the acetic acid formed, using the method of KUHN and D'ORSA, 1931; and KUHN and ROTH, 1933. In this way cuproxam lignin was first found to yield 6% acetic acid (FR. and SOHNS, 1933), but the values varied widely depending on the method used. If the chromic acid lignin mixture is kept for 2 days at a lukewarm temperature and then gradually heated after addition of sulfuric acid, the yield of acetic acid is reduced. Only 1,4% acetic acid was obtained with aqueous ozone (FR. and SOHNS, 1933). By micro C-methyl determination (WIESENBERGER, 1942, 1947) only 1% acetic acid was obtained from cuproxam lignin of both spruce and beech (FR. and G. DIETRICH, 1949). This led to the assumption that all the C-methyl groups were artifacts, produced by allylic rearrangements (FR., 1954), which occured during isolation and analysis of the lignin (cf. p. 64).

Artificial lignin enzymatically prepared from coniferyl alcohol (which contains no C-methyl) gives the same yield of acetic acid as natural lignin (FR., 1949, 1959). This seems to be the best proof for the formation of C-methyl groups during the chemical treatments. It was therefore concluded that before the treatment of the lignin with acid there were few, if any, C-methyl groups in the material.

2. Oxidation to Vanillin and Allied Materials

In 1904, GRAFE obtained a minute amount of vanillin by heating spent sulfite liquor with alkali (GRAFE, 1904). The yield of this product was later improved by systematic investigation of the best reaction conditions. KRATZL (1948) showed that acetaldehyde is simultaneously released from the side chain. Later it was found (FR., LAUTSCH and BRENEK, 1939) that the yield of vanillin is augmented if carefully controlled amounts of air are present during the alkaline pressure reaction. After modifications, this method is now applied industrially on a large scale in Canada and the USA. Disregarding the economic importance of this process, scientifically, the fact that about 10% of the lignin content of the liquor can be converted into vanillin does not say much more than that the portions of the lignin which affords protocatechuic acid on fusion with potassium hydroxide and that which yields vanillin are approximately equal. When spent sulfite liquors, lignin or even wood are oxidised with aqueous alkali and nitrobenzene at 160 °C, much higher yields of vanillin are obtained (FR. and LAUTSCH, 1939; FR., 1939 a; FR., LAUTSCH and ENGLER, 1940). Sprucewood gives the best yield. Essentially the same procedure was published in 1940 by SCHULZE. The yield was increased by LEOPOLD and MALMSTRÖM (1951;

LEOPOLD, 1952, 1952 a, 1952 b) who obtained 27.5% vanillin, 0.23% 5-formylvanillin, 0.8% dehydrodivanillin, 4.8% vanillic acid, 0.25% hydroxybenzaldehyde and 0.06% syringaldehyde. Later PEW (1955) found with model substances that dehydrodivanillin was obtained exclusively from compounds having the biphenyl carbon skeleton. The yield of substances derived from coniferyl alcohol can be calculated to be as high as 49% by allowing for the fact that spruce lignin (mol. weight of the unit = 183) contains not more than about 80% of the coniferyl component.

Hardwoods and hardwood lignins afford more syringaldehyde than vanillin, although it was found later that there are about equal amounts of coniferyl and sinapyl units in beech lignin. The lower yield of vanillin is due to the fact that the coniferyl units are more strongly condensed than the sinapyl units, whose 5-position is blocked by the additional methoxyl group. The *p*-coumaryl components of all lignins are even more highly condensed but nevertheless give rise to minute amounts of *p*-hydroxybenzaldehyde. Consequently, the relative yields of the aldehydes form a poor standard for judging the relative amounts of the three different phenylpropanoid components of the lignin.

The fact mentioned above that only 49% of the coniferyl portion of spruce lignin occurs in guaiacyl derivatives obtained by oxidation of spruce lignin with nitrobenzene is due to the condensation of its coniferyl units to biphenyl derivatives and other C–C-bonded products.

3. Other Oxidation Products

On oxidation of hydrochloric acid lignin with hydrogen peroxide in neutral solution, RICHTZENHAIN (1942) obtained small amounts of tricarballylic acid (*22*) (propane-1,2,3-tricarboxylic acid) and *β*-hydroxyglutaric acid (*23*). The formation of the former compound can now be explained from the known constitution of lignin given below. Vanillin does not give rise to either acid. However, since RICHTZENHAIN confirmed an earlier finding of ANDERZÉN and HOLMBERG (1923) that both lignin and vanillin gave rise to succinic acid by the same method, it must be assumed that very complicated changes take place. Moreover, the formation of (*23*) has not been proved with a lignin that has not been in contact with acid.

By oxidation of conifer lignin, READ and PURVES (1952) obtained a minute quantity of benzenepentacarboxylic acid. The degradation of lignin to methoxylated benzenecarbocyclic acids is discussed later (p. 78).

4. Hydrogenation

The hydrogenation of lignin and lignosulfonates has been investigated repeatedly over the past decades, mainly for technical reasons. Here our interest must be restricted to results that have contributed to our knowledge of the constitution of lignin.

When lignin was treated with sodium or potassium in liquid ammonia (FR. et al. 1938; FR., LAUTSCH and PIAZOLO, 1941), small quantities of alcohols derived from propylcyclohexane were produced in addition to products with higher molecular weight. Similar results were obtained by SHORYGINA and KEFELI (1948).

Using a copper chromite catalyst, HARRIS, D'IANNI and ADKINS (1938) obtained cyclohexylpropanols and diols with hydroxyls in the 4-position of the cyclohexyl ring and at the end of the propyl side chain. In addition they also obtained C_{18} alcohols and reduced material of higher molecular weights.

Nickel carbonyl was decomposed by heat in the presence of spruce lignin, which had been prepared with acids. In this way the metal was finely distributed on the surface of the lignin. The whole was then dry distilled in a stream of hydrogen (FR. and ADAM, 1941); 40% of the material distilled over. The distillate contained 25% known phenols of the benzene series, 2.5% phenol alkyl ethers and a total of 2% of toluene, methanol, ethanol, and cyclohexanediol. In all, almost 30% of well defined products were obtained. Among the phenols, progressively smaller amounts of *p*-creosol, phenol, guaiacol, catechol, *p*-homoveratrol guaiacylethane were encountered, amounting together to 75% of the 30% of identified products; the remainder was composed of products of readily understandable condensations and transetherifications. Reduction with Raney Nickel see p. 77.

The hydrogenation of spent sulfite liquors to give sulfurfree oils (FR. et al., 1941; STUMPF, 1947) requires extremely drastic conditions under which any direct relationship to the original structure of lignin is lost. However, these reductions too revealed that major portions of the lignin are aromatic and irrevocably condensed.

5. Lignin and Alcohols

In the presence of mineral acids, the major proportion of lignin dissolves in hot alcohols (KLASON, 1893) with, as was found later, concomitant introduction of alkyl groups. The new alkoxyl groups produced in this way are stable towards alkali but are readily hydrolysed by aqueous acid; they were therefore considered to be acetals and ketals. This is only partly correct; the new alkyl groups are present mainly as ethers of benzyl alcohols: this was recognised by HOLMBERG (1936) from comparisons with model compounds. Benzyl alkyl ethers, and the benzyl aryl ethers found much later in lignin, are readily transetherified under these conditions provided they do not form part of heterocyclic systems. MARTON and ADLER (1963) found that 0.5% hydrogen chloride in methanol at room temperature is sufficient to raise the methoxyl content of lignin by 0.6 OCH_3 per C_9 unit. If the carbonyl groups in lignin are reduced with sodium borohydride beforehand, the number of new methoxyl groups introduced is much lower.

Primary alcohols such as the cinnamyl alcohol group or β-keto alcohols (FR. and TORRES-SERRES, 1962; FR., LAUTENSCHLÄGER and TAUSEND, 1965) are also readily etherified and transetherified.

On treatment of wood with hot ethanolic hydrochloric acid, CRAMER, HUNTER and HIBBERT (1939); WEST, MACINNES and HIBBERT (1943) isolated a few percent of the lignin as ketones of the guaiacylpropane series which were at the oxidation level of guaiacylglycerol or coniferaldehyde, e.g. 1-guaiacyl-2-ethoxypropane-1-one.

These degradation products are important because they are derivatives of phenylpropane and also because of their oxidation level. The C-methyl group in these compounds has been produced by a rearrangement (cf. p. 61).

F. The Elemental Analysis of Lignin and the Calculation of Its Composition

1. Introductory Remarks

Following the methods of BRACONNOT (1819) and others (cf. BRAUNS, 1952) KLASON (1908) elaborated a method for determining the amount of lignin in wood. He dissolved the polysaccharides with 70% sulfuric acid at room temperature. The lignin is left as a dark brown-to-black residue and must be freed from esterified sulfate groups by heating with dilute mineral acid. A detailed specialized procedure was later given (FR. and PLOETZ, 1940). STUMPF and WIESENBERGER (1940) also published a method for assaying the lignin content of woods on a micro scale. The methoxyl content of the lignin is not diminished by this procedure, but the product is unsuitable for chemical investigations except for elemental analyses. When milled-wood lignin is subjected to the treatment of the Klason lignin assay, it loses its residual carbohydrate content (p. 113).

According to the method of WILLSTÄTTER and ZECHMEISTER (1913), lignin obtained by treatment with hydrochloric acid contains several percent of chlorine. On the other hand the lignin obtained by using hydrochloric acid plus phosphoric acid (URBAN, 1926, 1926 a) is practically free of chlorine (0.3%) and is suitable for elemental analysis.

However, in comparison to milled-wood lignin and the lignin in wood, these preparations have undergone structural changes owing to internal condensations, even though the analytical values are not markedly altered. The analyses of spruce-wood lignin reported by URBAN appear to have produced the first reliably accurate figures for its composition.

The analyses of KLASON, HÄGGLUND and URBAN will be discussed on p. 69.

The best material for analysis at present is carbohydrate-free MWL. (BJÖRKMAN 1954, 1956, 1957; HARKIN 1966/67, p. 52). Since this material represents only 25% of the total lignin, however, there is a possibility that it is a less highly condensed fraction which differs from the bulk of the lignin in the plant. This possibility must still be borne in mind though it does not influence the elementary composition. The acetates of milled-wood lignins are also suitable for analysis. As a substance for analysis, lignothioglycolic acid (HOLMBERG, 1930) has several advantages; it has an excellent consistency and represents the total lignin of any sample of wood.

During the processing of the samples for analysis, neither the lignin nor the wood from which it is prepared must be brought into contact with alcohols. As mentioned above in connection with the preparation of MWL, it is also important that the wood powder be thoroughly extracted with acetone/water or dioxane/water (9:1 v/v) in the cold to remove soluble constituents (lignans, etc.) before the final milling of the wood under toluene (p. 52).

The lignin is suspended in water, which is then evaporated by vacuum distillation at a low temperature in order to remove all traces of organic solvents under mild conditions. The analytical sample must then be dried in a vacuum pistol at 110 °C over phosphorus pentoxide. When samples for combustion analysis are being weighed, especially on the micro scale, they must be protected against open air because well-dried amorphous milled-wood lignins rapidly absorb a few percent of water (Fr. and G. Dietrich, 1949).

In addition to carbon and hydrogen, the methoxyl and ash contents of the samples must be determined.

Following a proposal by Holmberg (1942; Holmberg and Gralén, 1942), it is now customary to express the analytical values on a C_9 basis; only then are they readily and directly comparable. This method presupposes that lignin is a substance of the C_6 C_3 class. Since it has recently been established that lignin contains a few percent of a 1,2-diphenylpropane derivatives (Fr. et al., 1965), it can no longer be regarded in its entirety as a phenylpropane derivative. However, until accurate values can be obtained for the content of diphenylpropanes in lignin, no corrections can be made for them. Moreover, a rough calculation reveals that any interference they cause lies within the limits of error of the elemental analysis (p. 82).

2. Expression of Lignin Analyses (Fr., 1962)

The ash-free experimental analytical values are % C, % H, % O and % OCH_3; when expressed in the relative numbers of atoms, we obtain % C/12.01, % H/1.008, % O/16.00 and % OCH_3/31.035.

The methoxyl content, which is normally expressed separately in analytical reports, must be subtracted here with its content of carbon, hydrogen and oxygen from the total values for these elements; it is then recorded as an independent factor in parentheses in the C_9 formula.

On recalculating these values relative to % OCH_3/31.035 = 1 and subtracting 1 O, 1 C and 3 H from each number of atoms, we obtain the relative numbers of carbon, hydrogen and oxygen atoms in the lignin that are not involved in methoxyl groups:

$$C' = \frac{31.035 \cdot \%\,C}{12.01 \cdot \%\,OCH_3} - 1 = \frac{2.584 \cdot \%\,C - \%\,OCH_3}{\%\,OCH_3}$$

$$H' = \frac{31.035 \cdot \%\,H}{1.008 \cdot \%\,OCH_3} - 3 = \frac{30.783 \cdot \%\,H - 3 \cdot \%\,OCH_3}{\%\,OCH_3}$$

$$O' = \frac{31.035 \cdot \%\,O}{16 \cdot \%\,OCH_3} - 1 = \frac{1.939 \cdot \%\,O - \%\,OCH_3}{\%\,OCH_3}$$

Basing these numbers on a standard of 9 carbon atoms (C_9) and using the common denominator, CD, we obtain for the number i of methoxyl groups/unit and for the number of hydrogen and oxygen atoms in the lignin:

$$CD = 2.584 \cdot \%C - \%OCH_3$$

$$OCH_3 = 9 \cdot \%OCH_3/CD = i$$

$$H = (277 \cdot \%H/CD) - 3i$$

$$O = (17.45 \cdot \%O/CD) - i\,.$$

The expression for the molar content of methoxyl groups gives the factor i with which 31.035 (= OCH_3) must be multiplied to indicate the amount of methoxyl $[OCH_3]_i$ present on the average per unit in the lignin. The molecular weight of the average unit in the lignin is

$$\frac{100 \cdot 31.035 \cdot i}{\% \, OCH_3} = 27931.5/CD\,.$$

For spruce lignin, an average composition $C_9H_{7.95}O_{2.4}[OCH_3]_{0.92}$ is found. In order to be able to compare the degree of oxidation of the lignin with the mixture of the three *p*-hydroxycinnamyl alcohols from which it has been formed, the oxygen content in excess of two atoms is subtracted from the formula, together with the corresponding equivalent of hydrogen in the form of water. The unit of spruce lignin therefore has the average composition $C_9H_{7.15}O_2[H_2O]_{0.4}[OCH_3]_{0.92}$. The 0.4 H_2O is mainly structural water, but a part is specious owing to the carbonyl and lactone groups in lignin. The figure 0.4 is therefore partially the result of our mathematical manipulations and is only important for revealing the oxidation level of the lignin in comparison with the cinnamyl alcohol mixture from which it originates. The average formula of this mixture is $C_9H_{10-i}\,O_2[OCH_3]_i$.

3. Recalculation of Analyses for Acetyllignin

Frequently the lignin for analysis is taken in the form of its acetate, which can be made by the procedure of FR., GATTERDAMM and BOESENBERG (reported by FR. and SCHLÜTER, 1955). In order to evaluate the composition of the original lignin from the analyses of the acetate, the acetyl content (% $COCH_3$) must be deducted by subtracting the corresponding amount of C_2H_2O from the percentages found for carbon, hydrogen and oxygen. The acetate is an adduct of C_2H_2O onto the lignin.

$$\% \, C_2H_2O = 42.036 \cdot \% \, COCH_3/43.044 = 0.9766 \cdot \% \, COCH_3\,.$$

The values found are % C, % H, % O, % OCH_3 and % $COCH_3$. In % C there is a contribution of 2 C from C_2H_2O. Similar situations prevail for H and O. Let C_x, H_x, O_x be the amount of C, H and O in % C_2H_2O. Then

$$C_x = \% \, C_2H_2O \cdot 24.02/42.036$$

$$H_x = \% \, C_2H_2O \cdot 2.016/42.036$$

$$O_x = \% \, C_2H_2O \cdot 16/42.036\,.$$

Now % $C-C_x$ is contained in (100 — % C_2H_2O). Consequently, the percentage carbon content C′ of the acetyl-free lignin is:

$$C' = 100\,(\% \, C - C_x)/(100 - \% \, C_2H_2O) = \frac{100 \cdot \% \, C - 57.14 \cdot \% \, C_2H_2O}{100 - \% \, C_2H_2O}\,.$$

Similarly, the percentage hydrogen content is:

$$H' = \frac{100 \cdot \%\,H - 4.796 \cdot \%\,C_2H_2O}{100 - \%\,C_2H_2O}$$

the percentage oxygen content is:

$$O' = \frac{100 \cdot \%\,O - 38.06 \cdot \%\,C_2H_2O}{100 - \%\,C_2H_2O}$$

the percentage methoxyl content is:

$$(OCH_3)' = 100 \cdot \%\,OCH_3/(100 - \%\,C_2H_2O)\ .$$

Note again that the denominators in each fraction are the same. The values of C′, H′, O′ and $(OCH_3)'$ are the analytical data for the acetyl-free lignin. Using the first set of formulae, the composition of the acetyl-free lignin on a C_9 basis can be calculated. Hence the molecular weight of the average acetyl-free phenylpropanoid unit in the lignin can be evaluated. The molecular weight of the average acetyl lignin unit is: 100 × mol.wt. of lignin/(100 — % C_2H_2O). The number. of acetylated hydroxyl groups in the lignin = (mol.wt. of acetyllignin — mol.wt of lignin)/42.036.

4. Recalculation of Analyses for Methyllignin

1. Using the first set of formulae given above, the analyses for both the original lignin and the methylated lignin are recalculated on a C_9 basis. Let us suppose that the original lignin has the C_9 composition $C_9H_{7.95}O_{2.4}[OCH_3]_{0.92}$ and that the methyl-lignin has the formula $C_9H_{6.75}O_{1.2}[OCH_3]_{2.12}$. The molar methoxyl content of the methylated lignin in excess of that of the original lignin (here $[OCH_3]_{1.2}$) is split into three parts: $(CH_2)_{1.2}$; $H_{1.2}$ and $O_{1.2}$. The hydrogen and oxygen values are then added to the carbon and hydrogen contents of the methyl-lignin. The formula for the methyl-lignin then becomes $C_9H_{7.95}O_{2.4}[OCH_3]_{0.92}[CH_2]_{1.2}$. Thus, 1.2 hydroxyls in the original lignin have been methylated, but otherwise the molecule has remained unchanged. Whether this is always the case must be tested for each individual sample, using this method of calculation.

2. Given: MG = Mol.weight of the unit of the original lignin;
Mol.weight of CH_2 = 14;
$\%OCH_3$ = $\%OCH_3$ of the original lignin;
$\%OCH_3'$ = $\%OCH_3$ of the methylated lignin.

Searched for: x = Number of the methylated hydroxyls of the original lignin unit.

$$\text{Construction: } (MG + 14 \cdot x) : \left(\frac{MG \cdot \%\,OCH_3}{100} + 31.04 \cdot x\right) = 100 : \%OCH_3'\ ,$$

$$x = \frac{MG\,(\%\,OCH_3' - \%\,OCH_3)}{3104 - 14 \cdot \%\,OCH_3'}\ .$$

5. Recalculation of Lignothioglycolic Acid

As mentioned above, lignothioglycolic acid is very convenient for analytical purposes. Experience has shown that about two-thirds of the thioglycolic acid units enter in their entirety (preferentially by cleavage of ether bonds) while the remainder replaces hydroxyl groups, i.e. about one-third of the thioglycolic acid enters the lignin in the form $C_2H_4O_2S — H_2O$. The thioglycolic acid combined with the lignin is therefore subtracted in the form $C_2H_{3.33}O_{1.67}S$. The experimental values are % C, % H, % O, % OCH_3, and % S. In 100 g of lignothioglycolic acid there are 86.12 %S/ 32.07 = 2.685·% S of $C_2H_{3.33}O_{1.67}S$. The carbon content of this "thioglycolic acid — 1/3 H_2O" attached to the lignin is:

$$C' = 24.02 \cdot \% \, S/32.07 = 0.749 \cdot \% \, S \, ;$$

its hydrogen content is:

$$H' = 3.36 \cdot \% \, S/32.07 = 0.105 \cdot \% \, S \, ;$$

its oxygen content is:

$$O' = 26.67 \cdot \% \, S/32.07 = 0.831 \cdot \% \, S \, .$$

These values and the sulfur content must be substracted from the original analytical figures. In (100 — 2.685·% S) g of thioglycolic acid free lignin there are:

(% C — 0.749·% S) percent of carbon;

(% H — 0.105·% S) percent of hydrogen;

(% O — 0.831·% S) percent of oxygen.

Thus the percentage carbon content of the thioglycolic acid free lignin is:

$$C'' = \frac{100 \cdot \% \, C — 74.9 \cdot \% \, S}{100 — 2.685 \cdot \% \, S} = \frac{\% \cdot C — 0.749 \cdot \% \, S}{1 — 0.02685 \cdot \% \, S} \, ;$$

the percentage hydrogen content is:

$$H'' = \frac{\% \, H — 0.105 \cdot \% \, S}{1 — 0.02685 \cdot \% \, S} \, ;$$

the percentage oxygen content is:

$$O'' = \frac{\% \, O — 0.831 \cdot \% \, S}{1 — 0.02685 \cdot \% \, S} \, ;$$

the percentage methoxyl content is:

$$(OCH_3)'' = \frac{\% \, OCH_3}{1 — 0.02685 \cdot \% \, S} \, .$$

These percentages are again used to calculate the C_9 formula using the expressions for a simple lignin. Afterwards the molecular weight of the lignin part of the lignothioglycolic acid can be evaluated. The molecular weight of the lignin divided by (1 — 0.02685·% S) gives the molecular weight of the average unit in the lignothioglycolic acid. The number of thioglycolic acid residues present (less one-third of a mole of water) on the average per lignin unit = (mol.wt. of lignothioglycolic acid — mol.wt. of lignin)/86.12. The composition of a thioglycolic acid derivative containing *a* moles of the partially dehydrated thioglycolic acid per average unit of the lignin is thus:

$$C_9H_{7.15}O_2[H_2O]_{0.4}[OCH_3]_{0.92}[C_2H_{3.33}O_{1.67}S]_a .$$

G. Analytical Data on Lignin

1. Elemental Composition

Quantitative analytical investigations of lignins and their derivatives made only slow progress for lack of suitable substrates.

Klason's first analysis (1908) was executed with a lignin prepared by the action of 70% H_2SO_4 on wood. A second and third one, published by Hägglund (1918) and Hägglund and Malm (1922), were performed with preparations obtained by the action of highly concentrated hydrochloric acid on wood. The next one was made by Urban (1926, 1926 a) who used a mixture (3:1v/v) of 36% hydrochloric acid and 80% phosphoric acid. The analytical data are given below, together with an average spruce lignin analysis and with those of coniferyl alcohol and aldehyde:

	% C	H	O	OCH_3	Cl
Klason	66.67	5.49	27.84	14.5	
Hägglund	65.47	5.47	29.06	14.3	free of Cl by calculation *
Hägglund and Malm	64.1	5.4	30.5	14.7	present?
Urban	64.62	5.75	29.63	15.45	0.3
Average spruce lignin	65.08	5.90	29.02	15.60	
Coniferyl alcohol	66.65	6.71	26.64	17.22	
Coniferaldehyde	67.41	5.66	26.94	17.42	

* It would have been better to substitute, by calculation, OH for Cl.

When calculated on the C_9 bases, the analyses bear the following appearance:

1908 Klason	$C_9H_{6.64}O_2[H_2O]_{0.25}[OCH_3]_{0.83}$
1918 Hägglund	$C_9H_{6.34}O_2[H_2O]_{0.44}[OCH_3]_{0.83}$
1922 Hägglund	$C_9H_{6.00}O_2[H_2O]_{0.64}[OCH_3]_{0.88}$
1926 Urban	$C_9H_{6.76}O_2[H_2O]_{0.49}[OCH_3]_{0.92}$
Average spruce lignin	$C_9H_{7.15}O_2[H_2O]_{0.40}[OCH_3]_{0.92}$
Coniferyl alcohol	$C_9H_9\ O_2\ [OCH_3]_1$
Coniferaldehyde	$C_9H_7\ O_2\ [OCH_3]_1$.

Klason's preparation had lost some water and may have contained impurities which depressed the methoxyl content. Hägglund's samples seem to have contained — like all "HCl-lignin" — a few percent of chlorine. Urban's preparation contains only 0.3% Cl, which is neglected. When compared with the average lignin C_9 unit, his analysis shows a deficiency of 0.39 hydrogen atom. If the hydrogen content in the analysis of the average lignin were 5.60% instead of 5.90% (difference — 0.3%), then the hydrogen in the C_9 average unit (7.15) would be depressed by 0.61 H-atom to 6.54. This means that the difference of 0.39 H-atoms between URBAN's and the average analysis lies within the limits of error of determination.

An analysis of lignothioglycolic acid given by FR., SEIB and DALL (1959) calculates as follows:

$$C_9H_{7.77}O_2[H_2O]_{0.44}[OCH_3]_{0.93}[C_2H_{3.33}O_{1.67}S]_{0.79} \cdot$$

Here the value for hydrogen surpasses the average 7.15 by 0.62 H-atoms. This corresponds, in the original analysis of the lignothioglycolic acid, to an excess (over average) of 0.24% of hydrogen. Here again the deviation lies within the experimental error.

The idea that lignin is derived only from coniferyl alcohol stood in the way of any stoichiometric approach to the lignin problem for a long time. For many years an apparent deficiency of methoxyl had to be taken into account without satisfactory explanation. This problem was only solved when the other *p*-hydroxycinnamic alcohols were recognised as companions of the coniferyl alcohol.

Conifer lignin is produced, as will be shown later, from a mixture of approximately 80 parts coniferyl alcohol, 14 parts *p*-coumaryl alcohol and 6 parts sinapyl alcohol. The composition of this mixture is $C_9H_{9.08}O_2[OCH_3]_{0.92}$. Thus a conifer lignin

$$C_9H_{\underset{-\,1.93}{\underline{7.15}}}O_2[H_2O]_{\underset{+\,0\,4}{\underline{0.4}}}[OCH_3]_{0.92}$$

differs from the mixture of alcohols, from which it has originated, by a loss of about two atoms (or somewhat less) of hydrogen and an addition of about 0.4 molecules of water. These differences are the most important characteristics of a lignin preparation (p. 81, 115). In the formula for the mixture of the alcohols, the content of H equals 10 minus the methoxyl content, e.g. 10 — 0.92 = 9.08.

Wood from one or two years old spruce twigs gives a lignin with a methoxyl content of only 0.7 to 0.8 per C_9 unit [FR., LEHMANN 1963, FR., TORRES-SERRES 1967 (cf. p. 98, 113)].

A difficulty encountered in the study of a high polymer such as lignin is that the qualitative detection of a group is insufficient. In molecularly disperse systems the mere detection of a hydroxyl or a carbonyl group is adequate and applies to all molecules independent of the yield, but in the case of lignins the question of the exact amounts of functional groups is of decisive importance. In the course of later work in the lignin field, the question was always how many ether bonds, ketonic or aldehydic groups, biphenyl bonds, etc. are present per C_9 unit.

2. Hydroxyl Estimation

The functions of special interest here are the total hydroxyl and the phenolic hydroxyl contents. The total hydroxyl content can be determined by titration according to VERLEY and BÖLSING (1901) who used acetic anhydride and pyridine. Their procedure has been modified by GATTERDAM and BOESENBERG (reported by FR. and

SCHLÜTER, 1955). Errors can occur in the titration if the lignin acetate coagulates. It is expedient to conduct the acetylation and the titration in a centrifuge tube. When neutrality is reached, the suspension is centrifuged, the supernatant fluid is decanted, and the sediment stirred up with a few millilitres of acetone and retitrated. The total hydroxyl content of lignin (1.32/unit) can also be determined from the acetyl content of acetyllignin. Here the transesterification method (FR., 1923) with its later modification (FR. and WEBER, 1925) is recommended; a micro-scale procedure has also been developed (WIESENBERGER, 1942, 1947).

The phenolic hydroxyl groups in lignin can be titrated on a semimicro scale according to BROCKMANN and MEYER (1953); (FR. and DALL, 1955; FR., HARKIN and WERNER, 1964) with sodium aminoethanol in ethylene diamine. The instructions for purifying and preparing the reagents must be followed literally. The reagent can be kept for only a few days. Non-cyclic *p*-hydroxybenzyl aryl ethers in lignin are split by this reagent and therefore titrated as phenols. The few ethers of this type present in lignin can be assayed by the following method (FR., HARKIN and WERNER, 1964): The phenolic group is methylated with diazomethane. The γ-aryl ether is now resistant against ethylene diamine and aminoethanol sodium, but it is easily attacked by methanol containing 0.5 % HCl. A benzylmethyl ether and a phenol group are formed. The latter is determined by titration.

When the water-soluble salts of lignosulfonic acids are used, titration of the carbon dioxide liberated on boiling the material with sodium carbonate gives accurate values for the phenolic hydroxyl (FR., SOHNS and JANSON, 1935). It has not yet been determined whether this process works also with solid lignin preparations.

The elimination of methanol from lignin by treatment with periodic acid was recognised by ADLER and HERNESTAM (1955); HERNESTAM (1955) to be due to a reaction of a phenolic hydroxyl group adjacent to a methoxyl group. This structural feature occurs in the coniferyl and sinapyl components of lignin, but not in its *p*-coumaryl residues. An *o*-quinone is formed and methanol is released. The latter can be assayed, or the *o*-quinone can be estimated by an optical method.

It is well known that the absorption bands of phenols in the ultraviolet are intensified and shifted toward longer wave lengths in alkaline media. O. GOLDSCHMIDT and simultaneously G. AULIN-ERDTMAN (cf. BRAUNS and BRAUNS, 1960) examined this effect with lignin models and transferred the results to lignin in order to determine its phenolic hydroxyl content. The technique gives good results with lignin itself; discrepancies occur with lignothioglycolic acid, perhaps owing to improper selection of model phenols (FR., SEIB and DALL, 1959).

The hydroxyl values obtained by these different methods are in satisfactory agreement. Spruce lignin, for example, contains a phenolic hydroxyl group in approximately every third unit, in addition to almost one aliphatic hydroxyl group per C_9 unit (total hydroxyl 1.32). Usually the content is indicated per C_9 unit; thus spruce lignin has about 0.32 phenolic hydroxyl groups per unit.

The remainder of the hydroxyl groups is aliphatic (about 1.0 per unit). The majority of these are primary alcohols (about 0.75 per unit), while the rest are secondary alcohols (about 0.25 per unit), most of them being *p*-alkoxybenzyl alcohols.

A fraction of the secondary hydroxyl groups is due to *p*-hydroxybenzyl alcohols, i.e. derivatives of 1-(*p*-hydroxyphenyl)-propan-1-ol. This grouping (less than 0.05

per unit) can be assayed colorimetrically using the indophenol reaction with N-chloroimino-*p*-benzoquinone. The indophenol reaction was discovered by Ziegler and Gartler (1948, 1949) and applied to lignin by Gierer (1954).

3. Carbonyl Groups

Lignin contains carbonyl groups (less than 0.2 CO per unit in spruce lignin). These react with hydroxylamine hydrochloride; the hydrochloric acid released can be titrated. A minute amount, about 0.03 or less per unit, is of the cinnamaldehyde type and is responsible for the red coloration of lignin produced with phloroglucinol and hydrochloric acid (Adler 1948; Adler and Ellmer, 1948). The yellow coloration of wood produced by aniline hydrochloride is also due to this grouping, but the yellow-red coloration with diazobenzenesulfonic acid is due to coupling promoted by the phenolic groups.

A precise assignment of the remainder of the carbonyl groups cannot yet be made (about 0.15 CO per unit). According to Adler et al. (1966), only a little ketonic oxygen is adjacent to benzene rings, the majority is at the central carbon of the side chain. A very small amount of carbonyl belongs to a quinonoid system.

Free carboxyl groups cannot be detected in lignin, but infrared spectra reveal that lignin contains a minute amount of lactone (about 0.06 lactone oxygen per unit).

4. Ether Oxygen and Oxygen Balance

The distribution of the ether oxygen is one of the most important features of lignin chemistry. In spruce lignin — which is the lignin under discussion here unless indicated otherwise — each unit contains 2.4 atoms of oxygen over and above the methoxyl content. The distribution of this oxygen — with no claim to accuracy in the second decimal place — is as shown in Table 1. (Fr., 1964; Fr. and Harkin, 1964; Fr., 1964/5).

The first numbers are determined directly or indirectly; the numbers in parentheses are calculated from the schematic constitution p. 75.

The following comments must be made on the entries in Table 1:

1. This figure assumes that each unit is a derivative of *p*-hydroxyphenylpropane. This is one of the most important statements in this entire publication, it will be proved later (e.g. p. 65, 82).

3. The sum 0.84 of the ether oxygen (entries 3 and 18) represents that portion of the total oxygen (2.4 O per unit) which is neither hydroxyl (1.32), carbonyl (0.20) nor lactone (0.04) oxygen. The value of 0.84 is obtained by difference and includes a small amount of aliphatic ether oxygen belonging to pinoresinol and pinoresinolide estimated at about 0.18 O per unit (entry 18); but its main part (0.66) is due to aliphatic aromatic ethers (see below). The value of 0.66 results from both subtraction of entry 2 from entry 1 and subtraction of entry 18 from the total ether oxygen (0.84).

4. The figure 0.17 is the sum of entries 5, 6, and 7.

5. The figure 0.09 corresponds to half of the dehydrodiconiferyl alcohol units present in lignin, a fraction which is approximately equivalent to the number of pinoresinol units in lignin (see below). ADLER et al. (1966) find 0.09.

Table 1. *Distribution of oxygen, except methoxyl*

1. On the benzene ring				1.0
2. Fraction of 1: free phenolic OH			0.32 (0.32)	
3. Fraction of 1: etherified phenol			0.66 (0.67)	
4. Fraction of 3: benzyl aryl ethers		0.17 (0.18)		
5. Fraction of 4: benzyl aryl ether, cyclic	0.09 (0.06)			
6. Fraction of 4: *p*-hydroxybenzyl aryl ether, not cyclic	0.02 (0.06)			
7. Fraction of 4: *p*-alkoxybenzyl aryl ether, not cyclic	0.06 (0.06)			
8. Fraction of 3: alkyl aryl ether, not benzyl		0.44 (0.39)		
9. Fraction of 3: diaryl ethers		0.06 (0.06)		
10. In the side chain				1.4
11. Fraction of 10: aliphatic hydroxyl			1.0 (1.01)	
12. Fraction of 11: primary hydroxyl		0.75 (0.81)		
13. Fraction of 11: secondary hydroxyl		0.25 (0.20)		
14. Fraction of 10: carbonyl			0.20 (0.19)	
15. Fraction of 14: aldehyde		0.03 (0.03)		
16. Fraction of 14: ketone		0.17 (0.16)		
17. Fraction of 10: lactone			0.04 (0.03)	
18. Fraction of 10: dialkyl ethers			0.18 (0.11)	
19. Total oxygen				2.4

6. and 7. These values have been measured (FR., HARKIN and WERNER, 1964; ADLER et al., 1966). ADLER claims 0.02 and 0.06. The value for entry 6 (0.06) is a consequence of depicting an entire unit of that kind in the schematic constitution; in a larger scheme it could be adjusted to the experimental finding. The same holds for entry 5.

8. This is the largest fraction of the ether oxygen, as will become apparent from the observations reported later. The figure 0.44 is the difference between 0.66 (entry 3) and entries 4 plus 9.

9. This is only an estimate (1 unit of 18), but the amount of such groups is not as low as was accepted formerly.

10. The oxygen attached to the side chain is the difference between the total oxygen (2.40) and that attached to the benzene ring excepting methoxyl (0.32 + 0.66 + 0.02); 0.02 is a ketogroup as depicted in unit 14c of the schematic formula (*75*).

11. The aliphatic hydroxyl is the difference between the measured total hydroxyl (p. 71) (1.32 O) and the measured phenolic oxygen (entry 2).

12. The great majority of the aliphatic hydroxyl is due to primary alcohols. The figure 0.75 is either the difference between entries 11 and 13 or between the number of primary hydroxyl in the original C_9 units (1.0) and the sum of entries 15, 17, and 18. These three entries belong to the end position (α).

13. The number of secondary hydroxyls — no tertiary alcoholic groups can be detected — is estimated from the difference between the total aliphatic hydroxyl (1.0) and the primary hydroxyl determined by the second method in Note 12. In addition, the figure 0.25 assumed here is contained in the amount of methoxyl (0.39) taken up by $NaBH_4$-reduced spruce lignin with 0.5% HCl in methanol, according to Marton and Adler (1963). Their value of 0.39 per unit contains the 0.25 sec. hydroxyl, the entries 6 and 7 and the minute amount of benzyl alcohol groupings produced by reduction of conjugated carbonyl.

14. The total carbonyl has been determined by various authors, using hydroxylamine hydrochloride or sodium borohydride (Marton and Adler, 1963; Adler, 1961; Adler and Gierer, 1957).

15. The low content of cinnamaldehyde groups was determined colorimetrically (Adler, 1948; Adler and Ellmer, 1948).

16. This value is the total carbonyl minus the aldehyde (entry 15); entry 16 contains the minute amount corresponding unit 14c of the schematic formula (*75*).

17. The trace amount of lactones is due to condensation of ferulic acid into the lignin (see below).

18. The amount of dialkyl ether groupings is estimated from the pinoresinol and pinoresinolide condensed into lignin (see below); the minute amount of saccharide-lignin ether present in MWL is calculated as sec. OH.

H. Early Approaches to the Constitution of Lignin

(cf. Brauns 1952 a)

Although Klason's proposals concerning the constitution of spruce lignin were not precise and were frequently modified, and despite his lack of definite experimental evidence, the fundamental principle that he defended with great zeal was invariably the same: the close connection between lignin and coniferyl alcohol, from which it differed by a higher degree of oxidation. In his opinion the oxidation level of lignin corresponded in part to that of coniferaldehyde and in part to a stage lying between coniferaldehyde and coniferyl alcohol. He designated lignin as a polymeric substance, but nonetheless he sought after formulae of molecularly disperse oligomers. He did not state how these were supposed to be converted into polymers, for this lay beyond the concepts of that time. Klason also mentioned that his analytical data for lignin (p. 69) were in accordance with his belief that spruce lignin is an oxidation product of coniferyl alcohol.

The large proportion of ether oxygen in lignin became first apparent in 1926 (Urban, 1926, 1926a; Fr. and Hess, 1926). This knowledge influenced all later theories concerning the constitution of lignin.

A first assumption was the involvement of the primary alcoholic hydroxyl group of the original coniferyl alcohol in ether bonds with the phenolic hydroxyls, for these were mainly etherified. In order to account for the oxidation level of conifer lignin, the olefinic group of the coniferyl alcohol was assumed to be replaced by glycol residues. This resulted in the formulation of partially etherified guaiacyl-glycerin for the basic skeleton of spruce lignin (Fr., 1928 a; Fr., Zocher and Dürr, 1929; Fr. and Dürr, 1932). However, the oxygen and hydrogen content remained too high. To correct for this, about half a molecule of water per C_9 unit had to be subtracted. Allowance was made for this by inclusion of enol or keto groups or by assumption of condensations and cyclic etherifications. Suitable structures in the form of pyranoid or furanoid systems could be envisaged for the latter; for this reason, hydrocoumarans were taken into consideration in 1928 (Fr., 1928).

These speculations were all efforts to account for the ether oxygen in the lignin. Despite the provisional nature of these developments, etherified guaiacylglycerol was later recognised to be in fact a significant constituent of lignin. Recently, a small amount of guaiacylglycerol has even been obtained by cautious hydrolysis of lignin (Nimz in Fr. et al., 1965; Nimz, 1966 a).

A second lead came from another direction. In 1908 Cousin and Hérissey (1908, 1909) had found that two molecules of isoeugenol could be condensed by reaction with iron-(III)-chloride, with loss of two atoms of hydrogen, to give a crystalline product which they named dehydrodiisoeugenol. They also discovered that dehydrogenases from fungi produced the same effect as the iron salt. The formula proposed by the French authors was corrected in 1933 by Erdtman (1933, 1933 a, 1935, 1939): he interpreted the reaction as being a phenol dehydrogenation and attributed the formula (*6*) to dehydrodiisoeugenol. On removal of a hydrogen, the isoeugenol gives rise to a free radical which is characterized by the three limiting mesomeric structures (*3*), (*4*), and (*5*). The formation of (*6*) can be explained by addition of (*4*) onto (*5*) with subsequent prototropy.

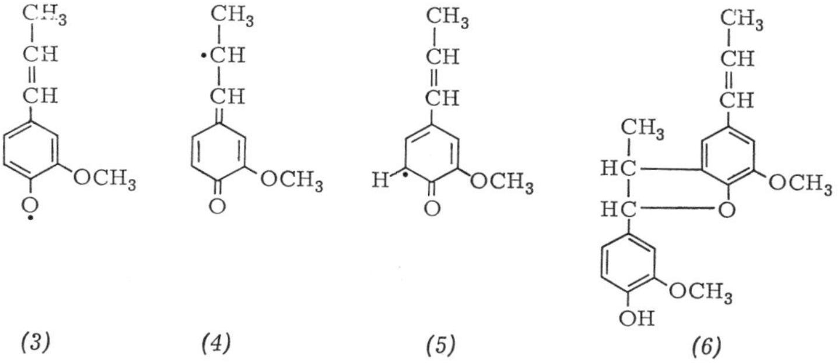

(*3*) (*4*) (*5*) (*6*)

A few years earlier, hydrocoumaran structures had been proposed as constituents of lignin (Fr., 1928a). Erdtman therefore transferred to lignin his observations obtained with isoeugenol and suggested that lignin arises by dehydrogenation of a guaiacylpropane containing oxygen in its side chain.

Thus, the idea of Klason and others that lignin originates by oxidation of coniferyl alcohol was characterised as a phenol dehydrogenation; this shed new light upon the genesis of lignin.

Shortly afterwards, isohemipinic acid (*8*) was obtained as a degradation product from methylated lignin (Fr. et al., 1936, 1938, 1939; Fr., Meister and Flickinger, 1937); it could also be obtained in the same way from derivatives of dehydrodiisoeugenol (Fr., 1939; Fr., 1939 a, b). In both cases the yield is only a few percent, but it was shown that a major portion of the isohemipinic acid formed was destroyed under the conditions used for the degradation of lignin. The procedure involved treatment of the lignin with hot strong alkali in order to split its ether bonds, and subsequent methylation and oxidation with potassium permanganate. This reaction proved that a structure similar to (*6*) must be present in lignin. Lignosulfonic acid gave rise to isohemipinic acid after methylation and oxidation even without prior hydrolysis with alkali (Fr. et al., 1937; Fr., 1939). This showed that a part of the ether bonds was opened in formation of lignosulfonic acids.

In the meantime, starting around 1935, Holmberg (1935, 1936) had carried out model experiments on the sulfite pulping of wood. He showed that lignin behaves towards bisulfite like benzyl alcohols and their ethers. Since dehydrodiisoeugenol and its derivatives react in the same way with sulfurous acid (Fr., 1939, 1939 a, b; Fr. et al., 1937), the analogy between lignin and coumarans received further support. Holmberg also interpreted the reactions of lignin with alcohols and hydrogen chloride and with thioglycolic acid as being due to benzyl alcohols and their ethers. Furthermore Hägglund (1925, 1926), Erdtman (1940, 1940 a), Lindgren (1952), and others (cf. Sarkanen 1963) showed that the sulfonation of lignin occurs in a series of stages; these were found to be essentially due to the reaction of benzyl alcohols and their aliphatic and aromatic ethers, all of which are present in lignin (p. 106/7).

As mentioned above, Holmberg also introduced the convention of basing the composition of lignin on its C_9 unit (Holmberg, 1942; Holmberg and Gralén 1942). Relying on the origin of lignin from coniferyl alcohol, the unit in lignin is ascribed the constitution of a phenylpropane derivative. The proofs for this point of view, which were not definitely established at first, became more and more numerous as the years passed, and took on a definitive form around 1960 (p. 70).

An argument in favor of this concept was presented from Hibbert's laboratory (Cramer, Hunter and Hibbert, 1939; West, MacInnes and Hibbert, 1943) (cf.

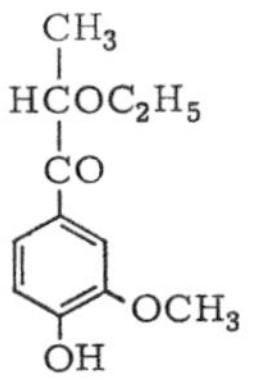

CH_3
$HCOC_2H_5$
CO
OCH_3
OH

(*7*)

p. 63). On heating conifer woods with ethanol and hydrogen chloride, ketones were isolated which all had a C_6-C_3 skeleton. The main compound had the constitution (*7*); its by-products were isomers of (*7*) or diketones. These were the first degradation products of lignin in which the guaiacylpropane skeleton had remained intact. Despite the low yield of products, the formation of these ketones is a good criterion for characterising a genuine lignin.

By reduction of lignin phenylpropane derivatives were likewise obtained by Brewer, Cooke and Hibbert (1948).

After the elemental composition of conifer lignin was expressed in the form of C_9 units, i.e. based on the oxidised or dehydrogenated coniferyl alcohol, it was observed that there was a deficit of methoxyl of roughly 0.1 OCH_3 per unit. This means that conifer lignin contains only about 90% of the methoxyl it should be expected to possess. This observation was later explained in a very simple manner (p. 70, 81).

By 1950 the chemistry of lignin was converging with greater and greater assurance towards that of natural phenylpropanoid compounds. These compounds include phenylpyruvic acid, cinnamic acid, phenylalanine and cinnamyl alcohol and their substituted derivatives. Around 1955, as a result of contributions from various laboratories, the origin of these compounds from carbohydrate metabolism via shikimic and prephenic acids became well established. This aspect of the chemistry of lignin is discussed more fully on p. 97f. and particularly in the part contributed to this book by A. C. Neish.

Part II

A. Degradation of Lignin to Methoxybenzenecarboxylic Acids and Other Products

The data accumulated up to about 1950 did not permit more accurate speculations on the constitution of lignin than the very general proposals mentioned on p. 74. According to HIBBERT (CRAMER, HUNTER and HIBBERT, 1939; WEST, MACINNES and HIBBERT, 1943) the ethanolysis gives only a few percent of C_6 C_3-units and even these are in an altered form. Potassium hydroxide fusion leads mainly to carbon dioxide, oxalic acid and protocatechuic acid.

The isohemipinic acid (*8*) mentioned above (FR. et al., 1936) is the product of a degradation procedure involving a combination of alkaline hydrolysis, methylation to protect phenolic groups and subsequent oxidation. This process gives many other products as well. Thus the yield of veratric acid is about 8% of the lignin content of the wood, that of isohemipinic acid is 3%. In addition, 1.5% of dehydrodiveratric acid (*11*), about 1% of trimethoxy-diphenylether dicarboxylic acid (*13*) (FR. and CHEN, 1967) and less than 1% metahemipinic acid (*9*) are also formed. The last acid was discovered by RICHTZENHAIN (1950, 1950 a) in about 1% yield on degrading hydrochloric acid lignin; but lignin that has not been in contact with acid gives only a fraction of this yield.

In addition to the 15% of the oxidation products made up by the acids mentioned above, at least 5% more of the crude reaction mixture consists of low-molecular weight aromatic products, many of which have been identified (FR. et al., 1965; FR., 1966; FR. and CHEN, 1960, 1967; FR., CHEN and CARDINALE 1962). These include the following substances.

1. Compounds of the Catechol (Veratrole) Series

I Veratrole. Based on the lignin content of spruce wood, the yield of veratrole amounts to a few percent; this includes minor amounts of veratraldehyde and acetoveratrone which are also formed. It is improbable that the veratrole is produced by decarboxylation of preformed veratric acid; it is more likely to arise from guaiacyl alkyl ketones.

II Veratric acid. Oxidation of methyllignin produces only about 1% veratric acid. On prior treatment with hot alkali followed by methylation, the yield rises to 8%, owing to the cleavage of alkyl aryl ethers.

III Veratroylformic acid. The yield is very small.

IV Isohemipinic acid (*8*) has already been discussed (p. 76) and is dealt with further on p. 101.

V Metahemipinic acid (*9*) is discussed on p. 78 and 101.

VI Hemipinic acid (*10*). The yield is of the order of 0.1%.

VII Dehydrodiveratric acid, i.e. 5,6,5′,6′-tetratetramethoxybiphenyl-3,3′ dicarboxylic acid (*11*) (Fr. et al. 1937), was at first thought to be a secondary product produced by the action of the alkali on the lignin. Later it was appreciated that the biphenyl skeleton is already present in the intact lignin. This biphenyl bond is probably also responsible for the formation of part of the isohemipinic acid (see p. 101). The formation of isohemipinic acid must probably precede the formation of dehydrodiveratric acid, for oxidation of dehydrodiveratric acid under the same conditions leads to only a few percent of isohemipinic

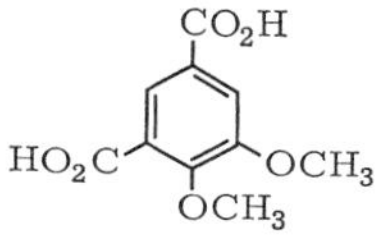

(*8*) 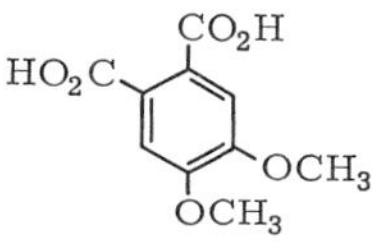 (*9*) 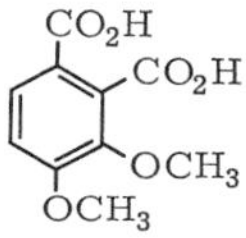 (*10*) 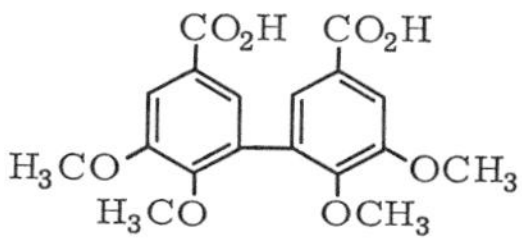 (*11*)

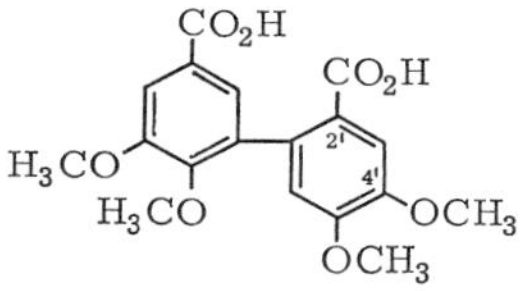

(*12*) 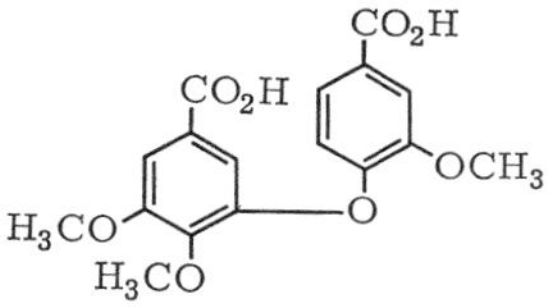 (*13*) 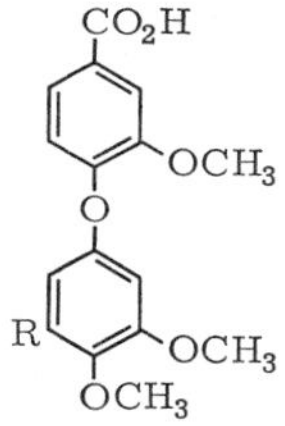 R = H: (*14*) R = CO_2H: (*14a*) (*15*)

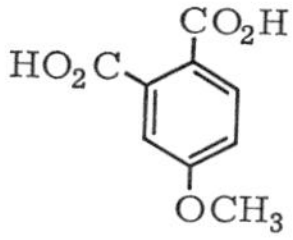

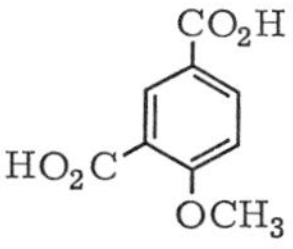

(*16*) 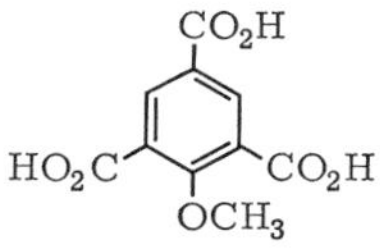 (*17*) 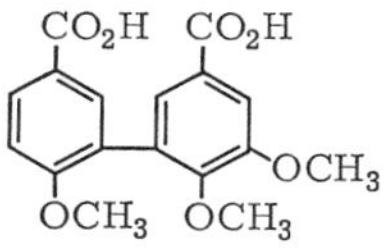 (*18*) 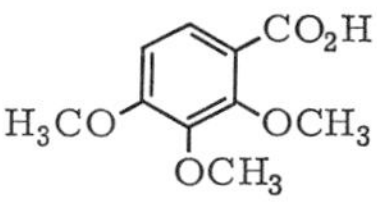 (*19*)

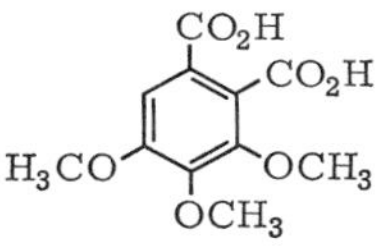

(*20*) 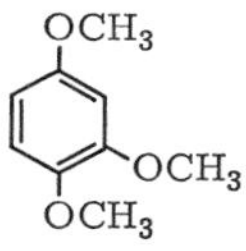 (*21*) 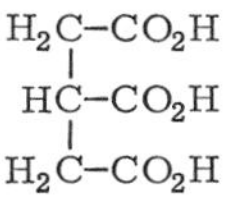 (*22*) 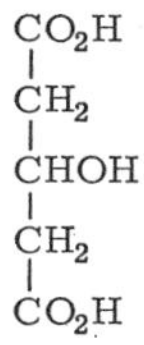 (*23*) 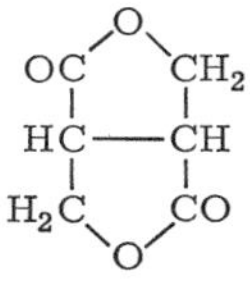 (*23a*)

acid. It is likely that a partially decarboxylated dehydrodiveratric acid derivative exists among the degradation products.

VIII 5,6,4′,5′-Tetramethoxy-biphenyl-3,2′-dicarboxylic acid (*12*). The yield is diminutive.

IX 2,5′,6′-Trimethoxy-diphenyl ether-4,3′-dicarboxylic acid (*13*). The yield has lately been found to attain nearly 1% (FR., CHEN 1967).

X 6,3′,4′-Trimethoxy-diphenyl ether 4-carboxylic acid (*14*). The yield is smaller than 0.1%.

XI 6,3′,4′-Trimethoxy-diphenyl ether-4,5′-dicarboxylic acid (*14a*). The yields of this and all the following substances lie under or around 0.1%. This means that all the acids derived from anisole or pyrogallol that are obtained from spruce lignin are formed in quantities that are much smaller than those of the catechol derivatives.

2. Compounds of the Anisole Series

XII Anisic acid.

XIII Methoxybenzene-3,4-dicarboxylic acid (*15*).

XIV Methoxybenzene-2,4-dicarboxylic acid (*16*).

XV Methoxybenzene-2,4,6-tricarboxylic acid (*17*).

XVI 6,5′,6′-Trimethoxybiphenyl-3,3′-dicarboxylic acid (*18*).

3. Compounds of the Trimethoxybenzene Series

XVII Tri-*O*-methylpyrogallol.

XVIII Tri-*O*-methylgallic acid.

XIX 2,3,4-Trimethoxy-benzoic acid (*19*).

XX 3,4,5-Trimethoxy-1,2-dicarboxylic acid (*20*).

XXI 1,3,4-Trimethoxybenzene (*21*) is obviously a methylated cleavage product that arises from the same type of structure that gives rise to the acid (*14*) (FR., CHEN 1967).

4. Other Oxidation Products

XXII Benzenepentacarboxylic acid was obtained by READ and PURVES (1952) in a yield of 0.2% of the lignin on direct oxidation of conifer wood in presence of alkali. A biosynthetic lignin made from coniferyl alcohol (FR., CHEN, CARDINALE 1962) also affords traces of this acid on oxidative degradation. It is readily decarboxylated to 1,2,4,5-benzenetetracarboxylic acid. The explanation for its formation is given on p. 89. Mellitic acid (benzenehexacarboxylic acid) has frequently been encountered but is formed only from lignin preparations which have undergone condensations before or during degradation.

XXIII Succinic acid is formed as an oxidation product from lignin (FISCHER, FRANZ et al., 1922/23) or vanillin (ANDERZÉN and HOLMBERG 1923). A Dakin reaction involving formation of methoxyhydroquinone from vanillin structures may be entailed (RICHTZENHAIN, 1942). α,α-Dioxoadipic acid might then be a further intermediate.

XXIV Tricarballylic acid (*22*) was initially found by RICHTZENHAIN (1942) on oxidation of hydrochloric acid lignin or cuproxam lignin. It also occurs in traces on oxidation of wood or milled-wood lignin along with the methoxybenzenecarboxylic acids. The presence of a lignan-type structure in lignin must be assumed in order to explain its formation (p. 89).

XXV The β-hydroxyglutaric acid (*23*) was only observed by RICHTZENHAIN (1942) on oxidation of hydrochloric acid-lignin. It is uncertain whether it is also formed directly from the lignin portion of wood or from milled-wood lignin.

XXVI α,α'-Di-oxymethyl-succinic acid dilactone (*23a*) was originally isolated from pinoresinol by ERDTMANN and GRIPENBERG (1937). It has also been obtained by OGIYAMA and KONDO (1965, 1966) by oxidation of the wood of cryptomeria japonica (sugi-wood), red pine and white beech. The two first species are conifers; the isolation of (*23a*) is a reliable proof for the pinoresinol entities contained in soft wood. In white beech both pinoresinol and preferently syringaresinol entities (*77*) are present. (*23a*) may originate from both of them (FR. and H. DIETRICH 1953, cf. p. 111).

This oxidative degradation reveals that, in addition to the major catechol-derived component of lignin, there are derivatives of phenol and pyrogallol in amounts that must not be neglected. If we revert to the concept, that will be proved later, that lignin originates from *p*-hydroxycinnamyl alcohols, then we can consider that spruce lignin is produced from a mixture of coniferyl alcohol ($a = 80$ moles), *p*-coumaryl alcohol ($b = 14$ moles) and sinapyl alcohol ($c = 6$ moles). These proportions are a rough estimate based on the yields of the various acids from the oxidative degradation experiments and on the methoxyl content of spruce lignin. First, $a + b + c$ must equal 100. Second, the percentage methoxyl content of this lignin must correspond to one OCH_3 of a and two of c (here: $a + 2c = 92$) yielding $[OCH_3]_{0.92}$. The relative proportions of the three alcohols that satisfy these conditions may be, for example:

$$a = 70\%,\ b = 19\% \text{ and } c = 11\%$$

or

$$a = 90\%,\ b = 9\% \text{ and } c = 1\%.$$

The following values

$$a = 80\%,\ b = 14\% \text{ and } c = 6\%$$

are more likely than the two others. For reasons which were explained above (p. 62) the direct oxidation of lignin gives less *p*-coumaryl component (LEOPOLD 1952, 1952 a, b)

Dehydrogenation of a mixture of the three alcohols in molar proportions of 80:14:6 gave rise to a biosynthetic lignin which was subjected to the same oxidative degradation (FR., CHEN and CARDINALE, 1962). Chromatograms of the free acids and their methyl esters did not reveal significant differences from those obtained by the degradation of natural lignin. Neither the types of acids formed nor their relative amounts showed differences. The latter can only be roughly estimated, however.

These considerations give an explanation for the deficit in the methoxyl content of spruce lignin compared to a dehydrogenation product of coniferyl alcohol alone as mentioned on p. 70. However, this explanation is strictly valid only if the entire methoxyl content of the initial alcohols is maintained in the lignin and if the phenylpropane skeleton of all the C_9 units remains intact during the processes leading to lignin. We now know, however, that both of these conditions are not stringently fulfilled. A very small amount of methoxyl may be eliminated by oxidation and a few percent of the units lose their side chains (p. 65). The two effects compensate each other, qualitatively at least, but perhaps not quantitatively. But it is certain that the loss or gain in methoxyl content caused by the combination of these effects is not analytically detectable.

The most significant result of the experiments described above is the proof that lignin produced *in vivo* in nature or *in vitro* by biosynthesis in the laboratory are as closely identical as might reasonably be expected of high molecular-weight amorphous materials.

The corollary of this is that lignin is definitely the product of dehydrogenation of a mixture of the three *p*-hydroxycinnamyl alcohols and therefore belongs to the family of natural phenylpropanoids.

B. The Dehydrogenation of Coniferyl Alcohol*

1. Introductory Remarks

Although up to 1950 there were numerous observations that would have to be explained by any constitutional formula for lignin, it was impossible at that time to give even the fundamental rudiments of such a picture. The prime importance of the C_6 C_3 unit had gradually become clear, but at the same time the diversity of the numerous observations made it apparent that in lignin two units were rarely alike. In contrast to the hydrolysis of proteins which produces simple amino acids or oligopeptides, there was no known method of degradation that yielded unaltered constituents of the polymer. Although the biosynthetic reproduction of natural lignin carried out in the laboratory was a great advance, since it gave a pure lignin without having to separate it from the other wood constituents, the artificial product posed the same problem to the structural investigator as the natural lignins.

Since degradation would not work, the course of the growth of the molecule had to be examined. Before this project could be attempted, preliminary experiments with model substances were necessary. Coniferyl alcohol and allied substances were used at first (FR. and RICHTZENHAIN, 1943; RICHTENHAIN, 1944, 1948, 1949).

* The lignin group of the Heidelberg laboratory acknowledges gratefully the great assistance of Miss S. SCHWAB, who synthesized some kg's coniferyl alcohol and other preparations needed for the work.

The enzyme used to effect the phenol dehydrogenation which was postulated to give rise to lignin was a crude phenol oxidase obtained from the juice of the common edible mushroom *Psalliota campestris*, for the mushroom *Russula delica* used by Cousin and Hérissey (1908, 1909) was not regularly available.

The mushroom phenol dehydrogenase was later found to be a laccase (Fr., 1957; Fr. et al., 1958; Higuchi, 1958). The range of activity of the enzyme towards the phenols related to lignification rose from pH 5.0 towards neutrality. Because autoxidation of the substrates by the molecular oxygen, which serves as a hydrogen acceptor for the laccase, begins at pH 7.5 to 8.0, it is difficult to estimate whether the laccase activity ceases at higher pH. A clear decision is also hampered by the nature of the mushroom extract, for heavy metal ions, which also catalyse the phenol dehydrogenation even when present only in traces, are difficult to remove or exclude from the system.

The intention to duplicate as closely as possible lignin biosynthesis as it occurs in the plant seemed to call for a slightly acidic medium for phenol oxidation in preference to an alkaline or even a neutral milieu. Satisfactory results were obtained between pH 5.5 and 6.5. Precise investigations of the optimum pH for lignin production, which need not be the same as that for phenol dehydrogenation of the pertinent substrates, have not yet been conducted.

To simplify the investigations of the dehydrogenation reaction, coniferyl alcohol alone was used as substrate; the number of products would much increase and they were more complex if the other two alcohols were also present.

Originally, the coniferyl alcohol was procured, according to Tiemann and Haarmann (1874), by hydrolysis of coniferin with emulsin. However, since emulsin splits coniferin rather slowly, Fr. and Bittner (1950) changed to "lubanol benzoate" as a source of coniferyl alcohol. Lubanol benzoate (Reinitzer, 1914) is a coniferyl benzoate in which the primary alcoholic group is esterified (Fr. et al., 1931). The benzoate is obtained in crystalline form from "Siamese benzoin". However, neither acidic nor alkaline reagents can be used to saponify the ester group without causing polymerization of the coniferyl alcohol. The free phenolic group was first esterified with *p*-toluenesulfonyl chloride, the benzoate then saponified, and afterwards the *p*-toluenesulfonic acid removed by stronger alkali. The yield of coniferyl alcohol is low. Moreover, genuine Siamese benzoin "almonds" are hard to obtain commercially.

After the discovery of lithium aluminumhydride, Allen and Byers (1949) synthesized coniferyl alcohol from ethyl ferulate. For improvement of the preparation see: Fr. and Hübner (1952); Nimz (1963); Fr., Swaleh (1969). The product is contaminated with a little unreduced ester, which can be removed by recrystallization. What is more inconvenient is the simultaneous formation of small quantities of dihydroconiferyl alcohol, which cannot be removed by recrystallization; it can, however, be completely separated by countercurrent distribution. After it was found that it forms mainly guaiacylglycerin-β-dihydroconiferyl ether [the dihydro derivative of (*35*)] during the dehydrogenation, its presence could be ignored in most experiments.

A saturated solution of coniferyl alcohol in water at 20 °C contains just a few parts per thousand. So only dilute solutions can be used for the dehydrogenation experiments. After it was established that in the plant, apart from laccase, peroxidase is also involved in the dehydrogenation reaction (Fr., 1957; Fr. et al., 1958), the latter enzyme, which is available commercially in pure form, was also used in the laboratory. It is immaterial for the production of lignin whether the enzyme system laccase plus air or peroxidase plus hydrogen peroxide is used. The lignin like dehydrogenation product (DHP) from coniferyl alcohol is formed approximately according to the following equation:

$$C_9H_9O_2[OCH_3] + H_2O_2 \rightarrow 1{,}6H_2O + C_9H_{7.8}O_{2.4}[OCH_3] \text{ or } C_9H_7O_2[H_2O]_{0.4}[OCH_3].$$

The loss of 1.2 atoms of hydrogen and the addition of 0.4 atoms of oxygen is expressed by the first formula. The second indicates the removal of two atoms of hydrogen and the addition of 0.4 molecules of water. Neither of these two formulations claims to describe the mechanism of the reaction; they only depict the composition of the end product. The second interpretation is preferred because the formula then clearly expresses the oxidation level of the units (7 atoms of hydrogen in artificial lignin as against 9 in the coniferyl alcohol).

Even if excess hydrogen peroxide is used, the dehydrogenation by phenol oxidation, after having led to the release of 1.8 to 2.0 atoms of hydrogen per unit, proceeds very slowly, although it never comes to a complete standstill. Since some of the hydrogen peroxide does not exert a dehydrogenating influence, the dilute H_2O_2 solution can safely be used in excess. We usually add 2 moles of hydrogen peroxide per mole of coniferyl alcohol. The excess either remains unused in solution at very low concentrations or is decomposed on the walls of the laboratory vessels or on the surface of the precipitated amorphous reaction product.

In practice (Harkin, 1966/67) the reaction is carried out, over a period of several days, by gradually adding a solution of 9 g coniferyl alcohol (50 mMoles) in 3 l of water and hydrogen peroxide (3.4 g = 100 mMoles = 4 equivalents in 3 l) from separate dropping funnels to a stirred very dilute solution of peroxidase (10 mg in 200 ml). The solutions are added at equal rates.

In this procedure the dehydrogenating agent encounters a gradually increasing concentration of dehydrogenation products to which fresh coniferyl alcohol is also continually flowing. This is probably much more like the process occurring in the plant than is the following procedure. In this alternative method highly dilute hydrogen peroxide solution is added slowly to a solution containing the enzyme and coniferyl alcohol; the hydrogen acceptor encounters all of the unreacted coniferyl alcohol, while the latter is gradually replaced by the dehydrogenation products. Here it was observed, unexpectedly, that all the coniferyl alcohol had disappeared from the system after only 0.7 to 0.8 g of H_2O_2 (for 9 g of coniferyl alcohol) had been added, that is, a quantity that corresponded to the loss of only 0.8 atom of hydrogen per coniferyl alcohol (Fr., 1964). The explanation for this is given below (p. 91).

Originally this experiment was carried out with laccase using atmospheric oxygen as the hydrogen acceptor. With this enzyme, too, it was observed that, just as above, all the coniferyl alcohol was used up long before each molecule could have been dehydrogenated and before the bulk of the insoluble amorphous polymer had precipitated from the opalescent reaction mixture.

This indicates that the consumption of coniferyl alcohol leads initially to a mixture of higher intermediates, still slightly soluble in water, which are converted by further loss of hydrogen into the lignin-like final products. In order to obtain a good yield of intermediates, it is recommended that the dehydrogenation be interrupted after addition of about three-fourths of a mole of hydrogen peroxide (1.3 g of H_2O_2 for 9 g of coniferyl alcohol).

These procedures offered an opportunity of examining the mechanism of the dehydrogenation of coniferyl alcohol with the hope of gaining insight into the mode of formation and thus into the constitution of lignin.

The first encouraging result was the isolation in 1952 of the crystalline dimeric lignification intermediate dehydrodiconiferyl alcohol (*30*) (Fr. and Hübner, 1952). It is made up of two molecules of the original coniferyl alcohol, which have each lost one atom of hydrogen. The detection of dehydrodiconiferyl alcohol encouraged us to investigate on a broad basis the intermediates of dehydrogenation of the *p*-hydroxycinnamyl alcohols. As mentioned above, it is much simpler to use only one of the alcohols at a time for the experiment. We chose coniferyl alcohol. Even so, the number of products obtained on dehydrogenation is overwhelming. Paper chromatograms indicate at a glance that at least forty substances have been formed. When isolated, either by countercurrent distribution or column chromatography (Fr. and Lehmann, 1960), many of these substances, which seemed to be individual species, were seen to be mixtures, expecially when recycling column chromatography was used. Nevertheless, it has been possible to isolate about 30 individual substances and to elucidate their constitution. Most of them are formed in yields of 1% or less, some in yields of a few percent, and very few in yields up to 15%. We call these substances monolignols, dilignols··· (oligolignols), and polylignols (Fr., 1963 a).

The general procedure for elucidating their constitution, after the elementary analysis, involves determination of the proportion of methoxyl to phenolic to aliphatic hydroxyls. Phenolic groups are determined by interaction with dinitrofluorobenzene and the aliphatic hydroxyls by acetylating the dinitrophenyl ether. Following the method of Brockmann and Meyer (1953) the sum of phenolic groups and *p*-hydroxybenzyl aryl ethers can be determined in many cases. After a brief methylation of the phenolic groups with diazomethane, followed by acetylation, the molecular weight can be determined. Such methyl-acetyl derivatives are frequently stable enough to indicate the molecular weight by mass spectroscopy.

The general procedure described here must be modified as the occasion demands. Examples are the lactones (*39*) and (*40*) or the *p*-hydroxyphenyl-γ-aryl ethers (*51* to *53*) and (*56*) (p. 88, 89, 91, 92).

The oligolignols undoubtedly give valid information about the formation of natural lignin. In nature, of course, the number of intermediates is expected to be greater owing to the admixture of the other *p*-hydroxycinnamyl alcohols. They intercombine — preferably with coniferyl alcohol — much as coniferyl alcohol does with itself; however, it must be remembered that *p*-coumaryl alcohol offers more, and sinapyl alcohol offers fewer, opportunities to combine, owing to their lower and higher methoxyl contents respectively.

2. Monolignols

When coniferyl alcohol is dehydrogenated, it loses its phenolic hydrogen atom to form initially an aroxyl radical R_a (*24*), which is also present as the mesomeric radicals R_b (*25*), R_c (*26*), and R_d (*27*) (FR. 1962). Of these limiting structures, R_b is the most favoured. The existence of the radicals in these forms is inferred from their reaction products.

In very dilute dioxane-water solution (1:1 vol.), the half-life of the radicals is about 45 sec (FR. et al., 1965). These conditions are not much different from those of our *in vitro* dehydrogenation (0.2% solution in water, 20 °C, pH 5.5 in the presence of laccase plus air or peroxidase plus hydrogen peroxide).

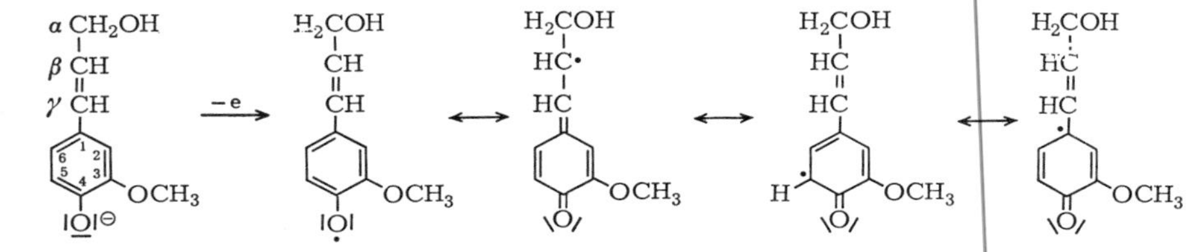

Coniferyl alcohol ion —e→ R_a (*24*) ⟷ R_b (*25*) ⟷ R_c (*26*) ⟷ R_d (*27*)

Other monolignols formed during the dehydrogenation of coniferyl alcohol are
coniferaldehyde;
trans- and *cis*-ferulic acid (*28, 29*);
vanillin (traces);
vanillinic acid (traces).

3. Dilignols

At a certain stage during the dehydrogenation, the dehydrodiconiferyl alcohol (*30*) produced is, at a rough estimation, about 15% of the total lignols formed (FR., HÜBNER, 1952). It arises by combination of R_b (*25*) and R_c (*26*). Since it originates from R_a (*24*), it is optically inactive. The same authors have transformed substance (*30*), after hydrogenation and methylation into the corresponding derivative of dehydrodiisoeugenol (*6*) p. 75. Both, (*6*) and (*30*), have the same configuration. No isomeric or stereomeric form of (*30*) has ever been encountered. The hydrogen atoms in the hydrofuran ring have the *trans*-orientation (AULIN-ERDTMAN, TOMITA, 1963). *Cis*-configuration has been suggested by LUDWIG, NIST and MCCARTHY (1964), but *trans* is more convincing. Though FR. (1966) quoted AULIN-ERDTMAN and TOMITA (1963), he adscribed through inattention *cis*-configuration to (*30*). This dilignol is present to a small extent in spruce cambium sap (FR., HARKIN, 1963) and by a procedure involving mild hydrolysis (FR. et al., 1965) has also been isolated in small yield as a crystalline derivative from spruce lignin.

Dehydrodiconiferaldehyde (*31*) (FR. and LEHMANN, 1960) is an unsaturated aldehyde corresponding to (*30*) and is formed in part by oxidation of (*30*), in part by condensation of free radicals derived from coniferyl alcohol and coniferaldehyde.

DL-Pinoresinol (*32*) (FR. and RASENACK, 1953) is formed when two R_b (*25*) radicals combine to build a twofold *p*-quinone methide in which each half has the same configuration. This means that a racemate is formed (*RR, SS*). By intramolecular prototropy a double tetrahydrofuran system originates, two additional asymmetric carbon atoms being thereby created. In pinoresinol these are again equal to each other (Erdtman, 1936) so that the benzene rings are in the equatorial position (Fr. and Sidhu, 1960, 1961). This means that when two radicals R_b combine, a transition state is developed in which the racemoid approach is more favored than the mesoid (cf. footnote p. 95), probably owing to some interaction between the hydroxyl and quinonoid groups. For stereochemical reasons, mesoid condensation of the two R_b radicals would allow the closure of only one ring. Such a product has not yet been found. Pinoresinol occurs in about the same amount in the lignol mixture as dehydrodiconiferyl alcohol (*30*). DL-Pinoresinol has also been found in spruce cambium (Fr. and Harkin, 1963). Using mild hydrolysis, Fr. et al. (1965) have found traces of DL-pinoresinol in extracted spruce wood. As mentioned above (p. 81) the presence of DL-pinoresinol is well established and not hypothetical as suggested by Pearl (p. 79 in his book, 1967).

DL-Epipinoresinol (*33*) accompanies the DL-pinoresinol in small amounts (Fr. and Lehmann, 1960). Here the configuration at one benzyl carbon atom is inverted to form an axial-equatorial system (Gripenberg, 1948).

The quinone methide (*34*) (Fr. and Schlüter, 1955) is formed by combination of R_a (*24*) and R_b (*25*). It is the prototype of many other similar quinone methides, especially those with higher molecular weights. It is yellow and can be easily recognized by its absorption maximum at 312 mμ and intense absorption extending into the beginning of the visible range.

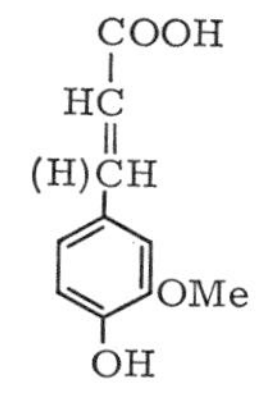

(*28*) *trans*
(*29*) *cis*
Ferulic acid

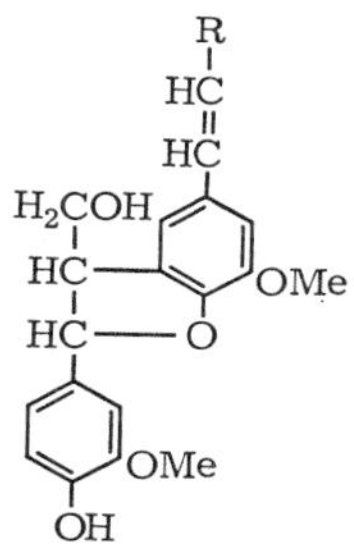

(*30*) R = CH_2OH: Dehydrodiconiferyl alcohol
(*31*) R = CHO: Aldehyde of (*30*)

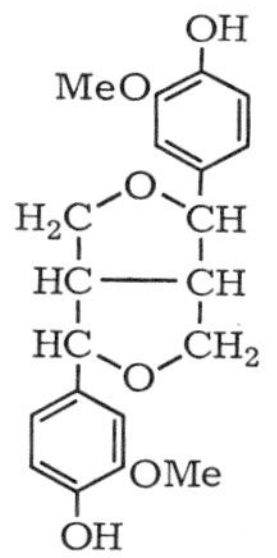

(*32*) DL-Pinoresinol
(*33*) DL-Epipinoresinol

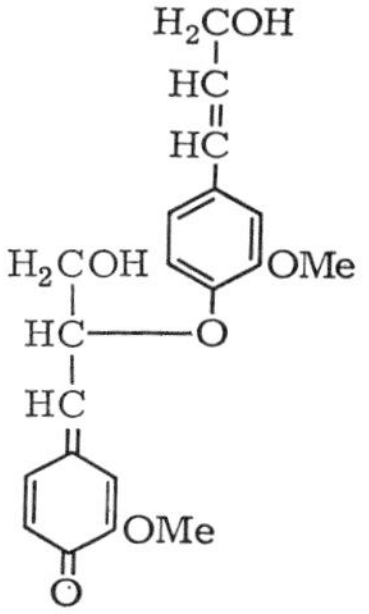

(*34*) Quinone methide

The same chromophore is present in the *p*-quinone methide precursors of DL-pinoresinol (double) and dehydrodiconiferyl alcohol (single). Measurements in a fast-recording Cary ultraviolet spectrometer indicated a half-life of the quinone methides of about 1 h (diluted solution in 70% aqueous dioxan at 20 °C and pH 5.5 (Fr., Grion and Harkin, 1958). They may become stabilized to a small extent by polymerisation [e. g. (*53*) and p. 94]. As the quinone methide (*34*) has no opportunity to become stabilized by intramolecular prototropy, it adds on external electrolytes, particularly hydroxyl compounds and, preferably, water (Fr. and Schlüter, 1955).

Guaiacylglycerol-β-coniferyl ether (*35*) (Fr. and Schlüter, 1955) probably surpasses in yield even pinoresinol (*32*) and dehydrodiconiferyl alcohol (*30*). So far it has not been obtained in crystalline form, possibly because of its labile benzyl alcohol group. A crystalline derivative has been isolated and also synthesized (Fr. and Eisenhut, 1955). Small amounts of guaiacylglycerol-β-coniferyl ether also occur in the cambium of spruce (Fr. and Harkin, 1963) and it has also been obtained, with minute yield, by mild hydrolysis of spruce wood (Nimz, 1965).

Guaiacylglycerol-β-coniferaldehyde ether (*36*) (Fr. and Lehmann, 1960) contains an α,β-unsaturated aldehydic group and is formed, in part at least, by combination of R_b (*25*) with a coniferaldehyde aroxyl radical, with subsequent addition of water to the resultant quinone methide. H. Nimz (1967 a) found it likewise among the products of mild hydrolysis of spruce wood.

Dehydro-bis-coniferyl alcohol (*37*) (Fr. and Renner, 1965) is a very labile substance formed by the interlinking of two R_c radicals (*26*). It can be isolated only as its tetrahydro derivative, which is stable. Corresponding biphenyl derivatives are formed preferentially from lignols with saturated side chains. The same must be assumed for systems with a 5,6-biphenylyl bond. The occurrence in lignin of compounds with such a structure is indicated by the identification of the acid (*12*) from degradation products of lignin (p. 80).

Diconiferyl ether (*38*) has not yet been isolated, but its presence among the dilignols is not inconceivable (Fr. and Renner, 1965). Undoubtedly, diaryl ether derivatives are also preferably formed by dehydrogenation of preformed oligolignols which contain saturated side chains. The occurrence of diaryl ethers in lignin has been proved by its oxidative degradation, for the acid (*13*) is also formed. Such ether bonds are more frequent than previously thought (Fr. and Chen, 1967).

Pinoresinolide (*39*) and lignenolide (*40*) (Fr. and Geiger, 1963; Nimz, 1964) are lactones, which are obtained in small yields from the mixture of intermediates. Both of them arise from combinations of dehydrogenated ferulic acid and R_b (*25*). They are crystalline and are responsible for the weak lactone band in the infrared spectrum of lignin.

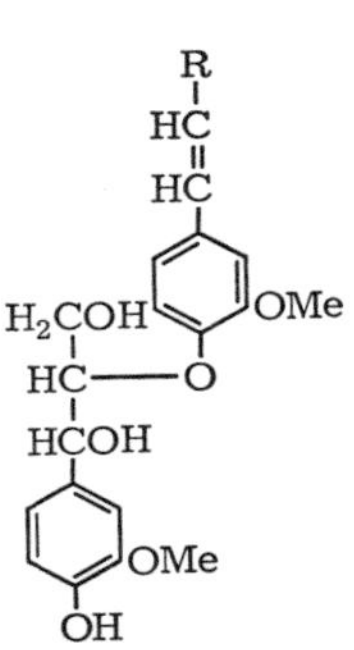

(*35*) R = $-CH_2OH$ Guaiacylglycerol-β-coniferyl ether
(*36*) R = $-CHO$ Aldehyde of (*35*)

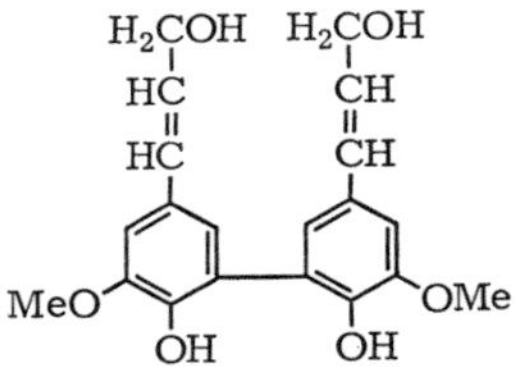

(*37*) Dehydrobis-coniferyl alcohol

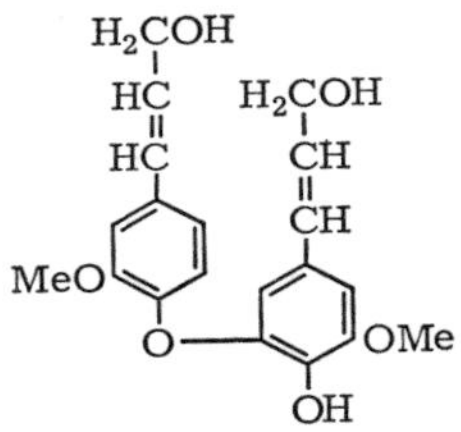

(*38*) Hypothetic diconiferyl ether

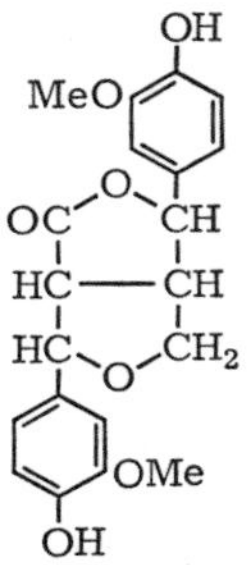

(*39*) Pinoresinolide

The lignenolide (*40*) may undergo a condensation between its double bond and position 2 or 6 of the other nucleus to form a cyclolignan (*41*), which is a tetrahydronaphthalene derivative and can give rise on oxidation to benzenepentacarboxylic acid (p. 80). Another cyclolignan, podophyllotoxin, also gives this acid on oxidation (SPÄTH, WESSELY and KORNFELD, 1932). A further oxidation product of lignin, tricarballylic acid (*22*), may originate from the same cyclolignan.

Here another possible explanation for the origin of the benzene-pentacarboxylic and tricarballylic acids must be mentioned. Spruce wood contains about 0.3% hydroxymatairesinol (*42*) (FR. and KNOF, 1957), which because of its optical activity is assumed to belong to the resin system of spruce wood and not to be a lignin intermediate. Nevertheless, it is present to a very small extent, in what we call "cambial sap" (FR. and HARKIN, 1963).

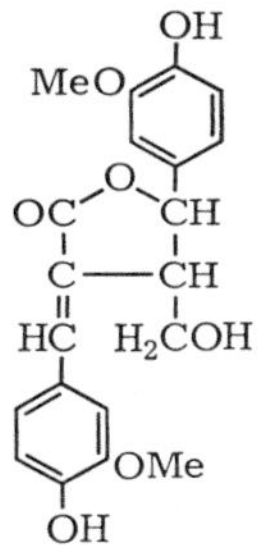

(*40*) Lignenolide 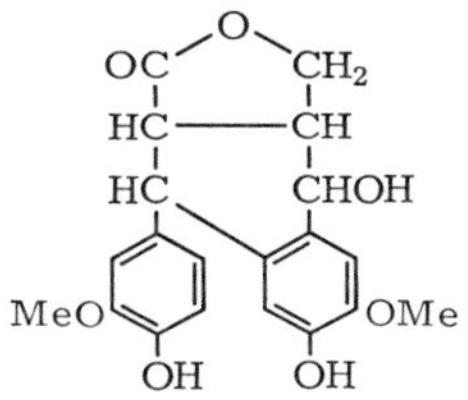 (*41*) Hypothetic cyclolignan 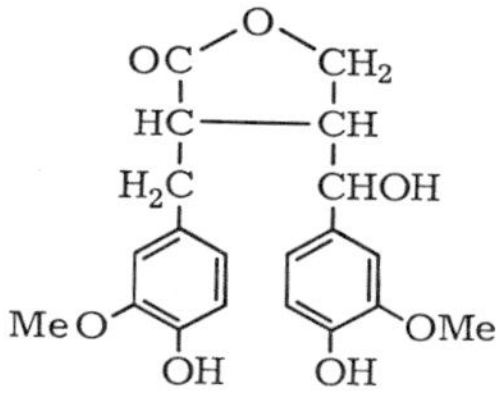 (*42*) Hydroxymatairesinol 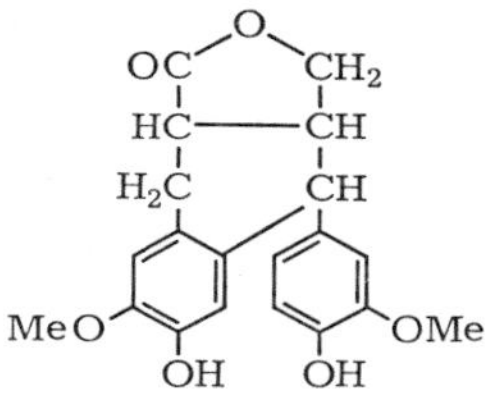 (*43*) Conidendrin

It is therefore possible that some of it may be incorporated into lignin. This substance is easily transformed by weak acids into α-conidendrin (*43*) (FR. and KNOF, 1957). On oxidation the latter may yield benzenepentacarboxylic as well as tricarballylic acids. This question deserves special investigation.

1,2-Diguaiacylpropane-1,3-diol (*44*) (FR. et al., 1965) is a crystalline substance that may be included in the list of the dilignols since it originates from two monolignols, namely by combination of R_b (*25*) and R_d (*27*) with simultaneous elimination of the side chain of R_d. Its presence among the intermediates of artificial lignin has been indicated by its transformation into 4,4′-dihydroxy-3,3′-dimethoxystilbene (*74*) (p. 97). The substance (*44*) appears among the products of mild hydrolysis of spruce lignin (see p. 96, 97). The diol (*44*), or oligolignols containing it, are present among the intermediates of artificial lignin formation and were also detected by their transformation into the stilbene (*74*) (FR. and NIMZ, 1966).

Coniferyl alcohol guaiacyl ether (*45*) has not yet been isolated from the mixture of the intermediates, but the presence of an ether of this kind must be concluded from the formation of the acid (*14*) on treatment of lignin with alkali followed by methylation and oxidation. Its origin can be explained by combination of R_a (*24*) and R_d (*27*) followed by loss of the side chain of R_d. 1,3,4-Trimethoxy benzene (*21*) (pp. 79, 80) may also originate from such a diphenyl ether. Acid (*14a*) indicates substances like (*45*) which have undergone condensation in position 5.

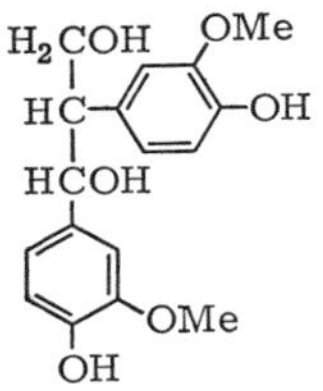

(44) 1,2-Diguaiacyl-propane-1,3-diol

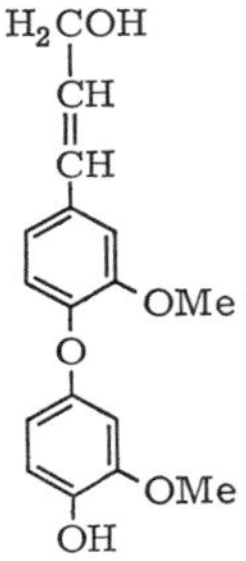

(45) hypothetic coniferyl alcohol guaiacyl ether

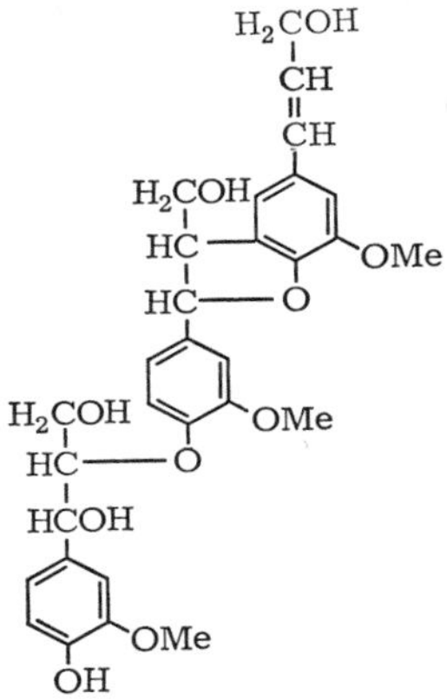

(46) Guaiacylglycerol-β-dehydrodiconiferyl ether

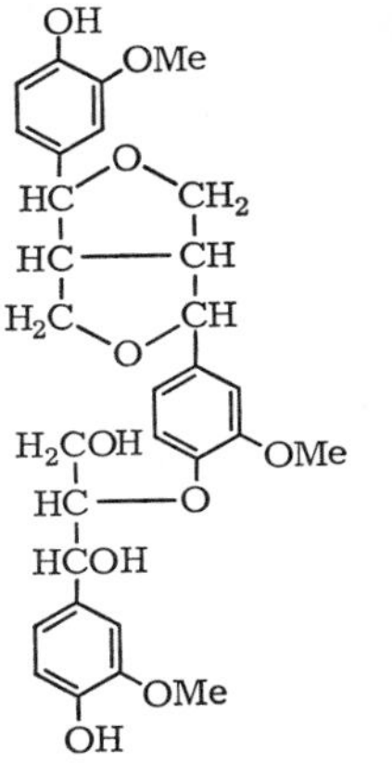

(47) Guaiacylglycerol-pinoresinol ether

(48) Guaiacylglycerol-epipinoresinol ether

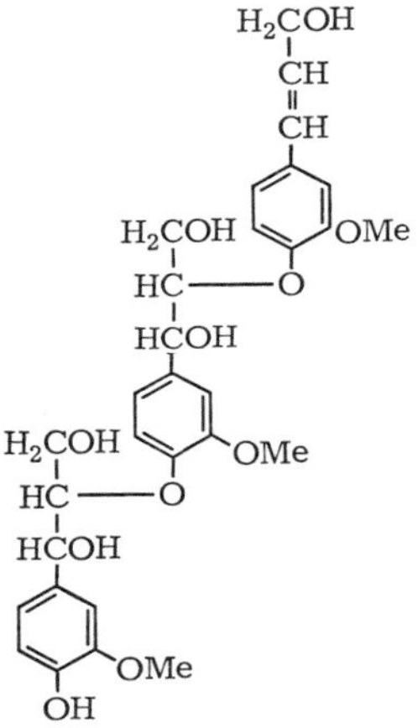

(49) Bis-guaiacylglycerol-β-coniferyl ether

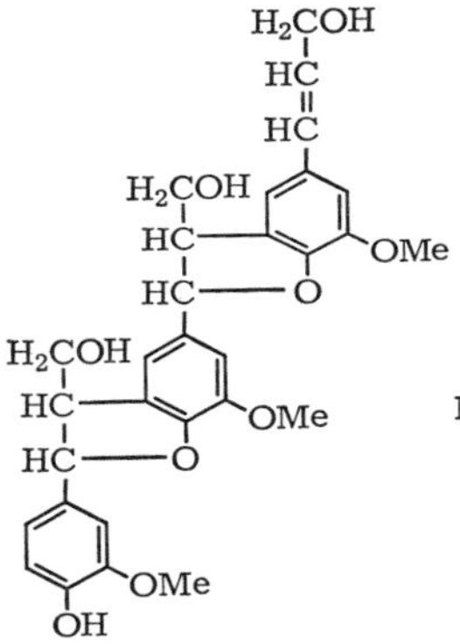

(50) Dehydrotriconiferyl alcohol

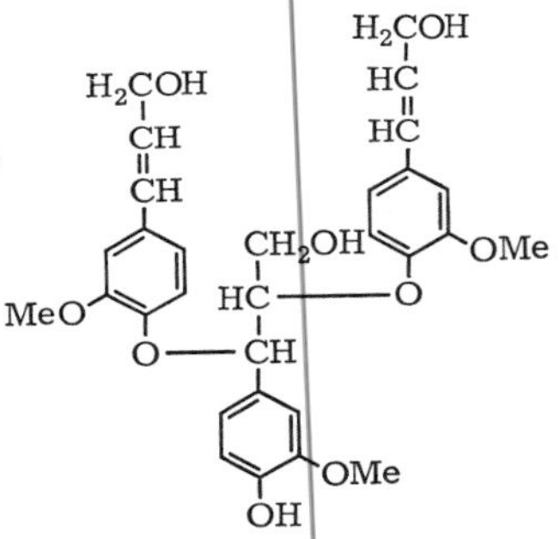

(51) Guaiacylglycerol-β, γ-bis-coniferyl ether

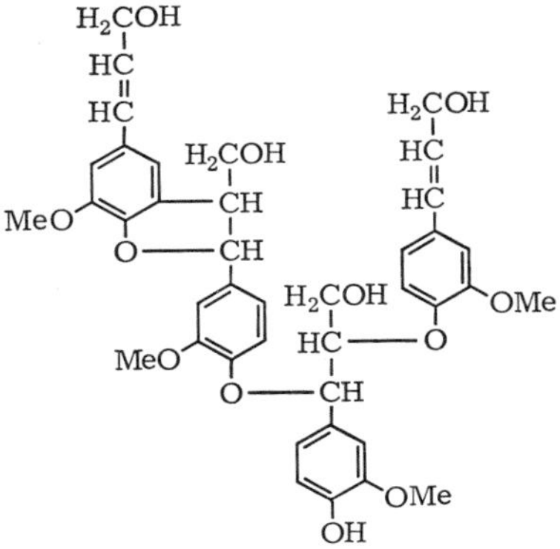

(52) Guaiacylglycerol-β-coniferyl-γ-dehydrodiconiferyl ether

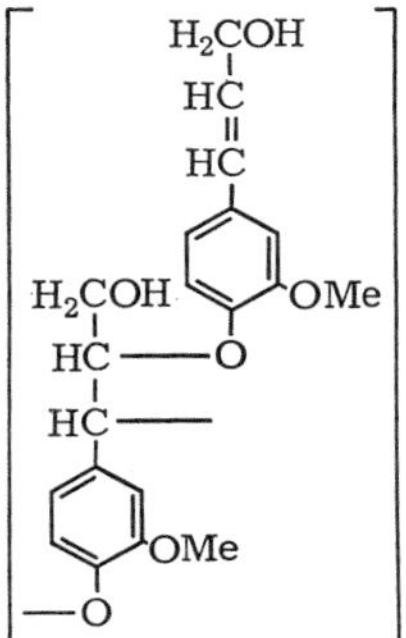

(53) Polymer of (34)

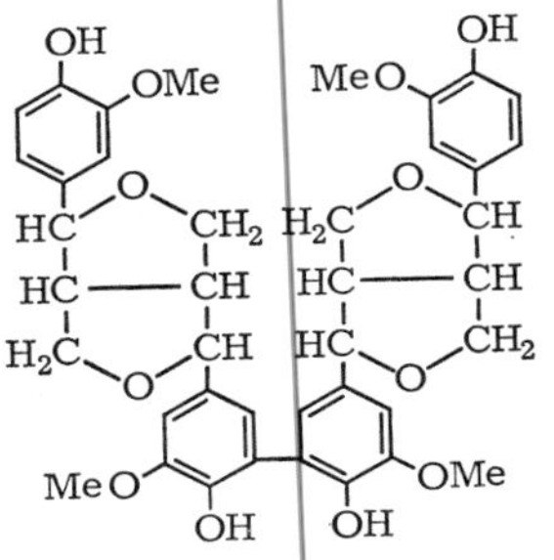

(54) Bis-dehydro-pinoresinol

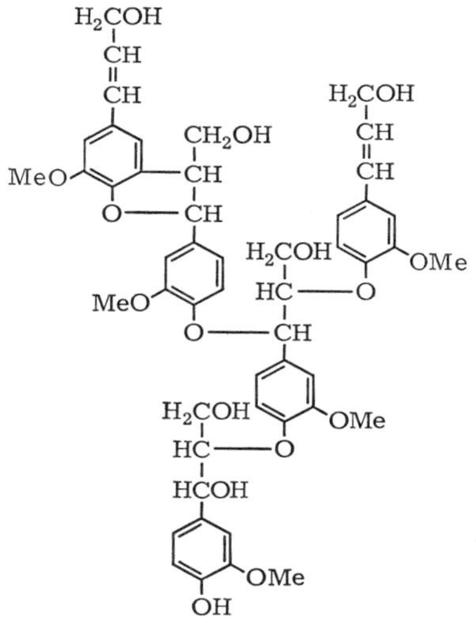

(55) Pentalignol, guaiacylglycerol ether of *(52)*

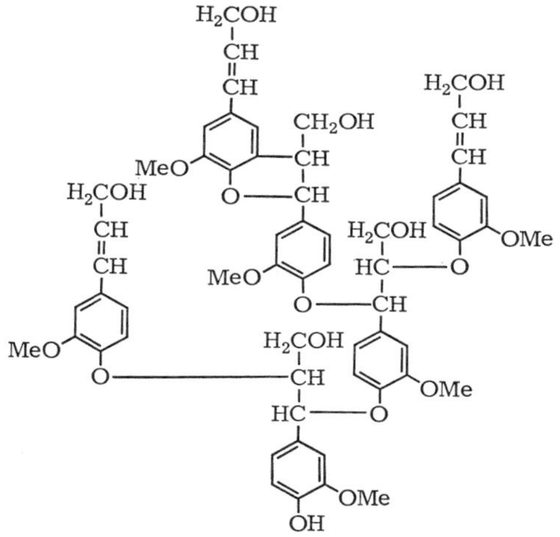

(56) Hexalignol

4. Trilignols

The members of this group [*(46)*-*(50)*, *(72)*] originate by combination of R_b *(25)* with an aroxyl formed from a dilignol by loss of phenolic hydrogen. The quinone methide initially produced is stabilized by addition of water. The trilignols formed in this way include guaiacylglycerol-β-dehydrodiconiferyl ether *(46)* (FR. and TAUSEND, 1963) and guaiacylglycerol-β-pinoresinol ether *(47)* (FR. and NIMZ, 1962). The latter trilignol is present to a greater extent than any of the others, and it has also been detected in spruce cambium sap (FR. and HARKIN, 1963).

Other trilignols are guaiacylglycerol-β-epipinoresinol ether *(48)* (FR. and NIMZ, 1962) and bis-guaiacylglycerol coniferyl ether *(49)* (FR. and TAUSEND, 1963). Dehydrotriconiferyl alcohol *(50)* (NIMZ, 1963) is another trilignol whose formation can be explained by interaction of R_b and a corresponding R_c radical of dehydrogenated dehydrodiconiferyl alcohol *(30)*.

Guaiacylglycerol-β-γ-bis-coniferyl ether *(51)* (FR. and FRIEDMANN, 1960) is a labile new type of a trilignol formed by addition of coniferyl alcohol to the dimeric quinone methide *(34)*. It readily loses a molecule of coniferyl alcohol by hydrolysis but is stabilized somewhat as soon as its phenolic group is etherified by further dehydrogenation and interaction with other radicals. It originates from three molecules of coniferyl alcohol by the loss of only two atoms of hydrogen. Oligolignols *(51)* [cf. *(52)*, *(55)*, *(56)*] are responsible for the rapid disappearance, mentioned before (p. 84), of coniferyl alcohol during the dehydrogenation.

5. Higher Oligolignols

Guaiacylglycerol-β-coniferyl-γ-dehydrodiconiferyl ether *(52)* (FR. and FRIEDMANN, 1960) is a tetralignol similar to the last trilignol and originates by addition of preformed dehydrodiconiferyl alcohol *(30)* onto the dimeric quinone methide *(34)*. It is more stable than the trilignol *(51)*.

Both (*51*) and (*52*) are *p*-hydroxybenzyl aryl ethers; so is the polymerisation product (*53*) (FR. HARKIN and WERNER, 1964) of the quinone methide (*34*) mentioned above. Such benzyl aryl ether bonds occur to a small extent in lignin and are easily attacked by acids or nucleophilic reagents containing sulfur.

Bis-dehydropinoresinol (*54*) (FR. and SAKAKIBARA, 1959) is a crystalline tetralignol formed by oxidative coupling of two molecules of pinoresinol and occurs to a small extent among the dehydrogenation products of coniferyl alcohol. Such 5,5'biphenyl-bondings occur frequently between other oligolignols in which the side chain is saturated, thus making the formation of radicals of the R_b type impossible.

The pentalignol (*55*) (FR. and TAUSEND, 1964) is a labile amorphous substance and is probably a mixture of isomers and stereoisomers. It seems to consist mainly of the guaiacylglycerol-β-ether of the tetralignol (*52*). The hexalignol (*56*) (FR. and TAUSEND, 1964) is an amorphous product that is more stable than the pentalignol (*55*) but consists of a mixture of stereoisomers. It is an adduct of the tetralignol (*52*) and the quinone methide (*34*). It can also be regarded as the adduct of dehydrodiconiferyl alcohol (*30*) and a tetrameric zwitterion or diradical formed by dimerisation of the quinone methide (*34*).

As of now the hexalignol completes the list of intermediates of the dehydrogenation of coniferyl alcohol. All the substances enumerated have been isolated and their constitution elucidated. Practically all the mono-, di- and trilignols have been sorted out. Others may occur, but they are probably insignificant. Only a few examples of the tetra-, penta- and hexalignols could be isolated; it is well-nigh impossible to resolve their mixtures.

C. Linkage of Lignin with Carbohydrates

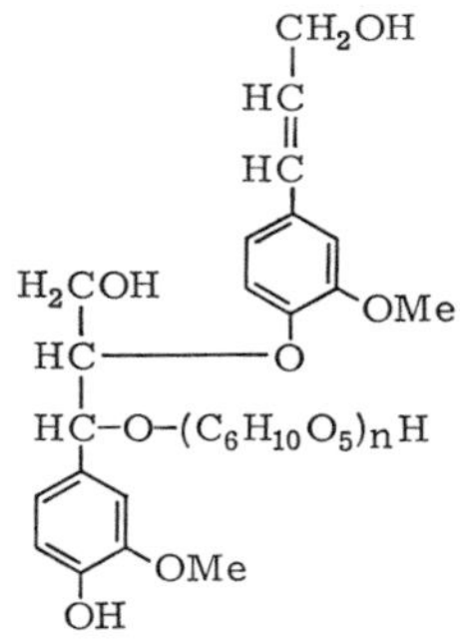

CH_2OH
HC
HC
H_2COH OMe
HC — O
$HC{-}O{-}(C_6H_{10}O_5)_nH$
OMe
OH

(*57*) Saccharid ether of guaiacylglycerol-β-coniferyl ether

Once more the reactivity of the *p*-quinone methide intermediates in these reactions must be emphasized. Their main representative (*34*) has been found to be able to add not only water but also phenols and even carbohydrates. The result is a new type of carbohydrate compound, namely carbohydrate *p*-hydroxybenzyl ethers [e.g. (*57*)]. These are about as sensitive as cane sugar towards hydrolysis by acid. Such a carbohydrate lignol ether is a phenol and can be incorporated into the lignin molecule after dehydrogenation of the phenol group, thereby becoming more stable. This is probably the main way in which lignin is grafted onto the carbohydrates of the cell wall. As a model, the adduct of sucrose and the quinone methide (*34*) has been prepared (FR. and GRION 1959; FR. and HARKIN, 1960). This was done by dehydrogenation of coniferyl alcohol in a concentrated solution of cane sugar. The adduct was separated from many other products, mainly lignols.

It is striking that lignin does not, in nature, develop in the absence of carbohydrates. The highest concentration of lignin (70%) has been observed by BAILEY (1936) in the middle lamella. It may be possible that polylignols are growing in the cell, especially when they are attached to the surface of the polysaccharides. In this way they would be unable to conglobulate and would grow to larger aggregates. Nevertheless, it is probable that the growth is limited when a certain size of the aggregates is attained and mobility and solubility decrease. It is explained below (p. 103) how such large entities are "glued" together by single units.

D. Quinone Methides: Benzyl Aryl Ethers in Lignin; Hydrolysis Products

In the preceding chapter it was shown that *p*-quinone methides are frequently formed during the dehydrogenation of coniferyl alcohol and that these combine with phenols preferentially to yield benzyl aryl ethers.

o-Quinone methides and *p*-quinone methides are assumed to be intermediates in the formation of phenoplast resins. These are formed in the warm reaction mixture and react further at higher temperatures. However, so far no benzyl aryl ethers have been encountered during this process.

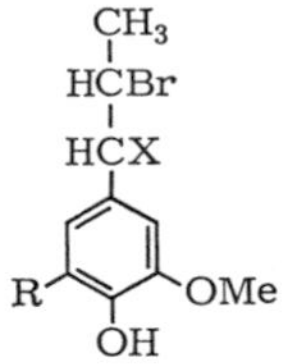

(*58*) R = X = Br
(*59*) R = Br, X = OCH_3
(*60*) R = Br, X = Cl

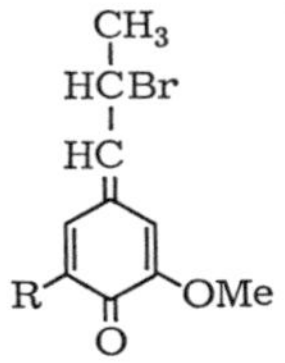

(*61*) R = Br
(*62*) R = H

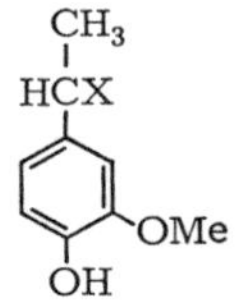

(*63*) X = Halogen or OCR (C=O)

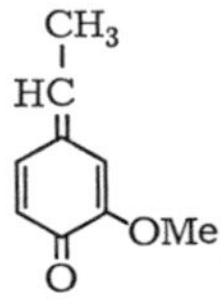

(*64*)

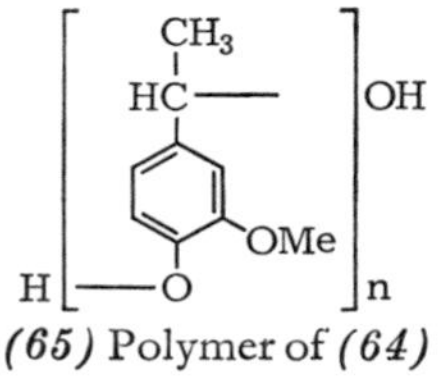

(*65*) Polymer of (*64*)

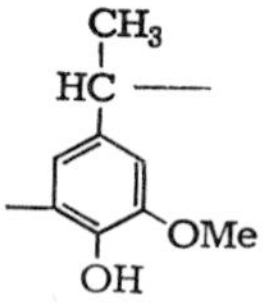

(*66*) Polycondensate of (*65*)

In connection with lignin, reactions that could be carried out at room temperature with synthetically accessible *p*-quinone methides were of interest. For a long time the best accessible crystalline quinone methide was the brominated derivative (*61*) made by Zincke and Hahn (1903) from isoeugenol via the tribromide (*58*). It is a stable yellow solid, which dissolves readily in organic solvents and reacts with methanol to yield the methyl ether (*59*). Its reaction with ethanol is much slower, but a trace of hydrogen chloride accelerates the formation of the colorless ethyl ether. Hydrogen chloride in ether decolorizes the quinone methide immediately by forming the chloride (*60*).

Later, preparation of the monobromo quinone methide (*62*) was achieved; it is more reactive than (*61*) (Fr. and Werner, 1964; Fr., Harkin and Werner, 1964). A simpler compound is (*64*); it is prepared from (*63*) and is stable for a short time in solution in ether but cannot be isolated (Fr. and Werner, 1964). Both (*62*) and (*64*) readily combine with phenols to give *p*-hydroxybenzyl aryl ethers. The ease of the

Table 2. *Rate of reactivity of quinone methides with hydroxy compounds*

	Rate	pK
Mineral Acids	immediate	
Organic Acids	fast	
Phenols	less fast	10^{-8} — 10^{-10}
Sugars	moderate	10^{-13} — 10^{-15}
Water	moderate	10^{-14}
Methanol	moderate	10^{-17}
Ethanol	very slow	10^{-20} or less
Higher Alcohols	extremely slow, if at all	

addition reactions of such *p*-quinone methides is apparently a function of the dissociation constants of the compounds being added (Table 2).

The behavior of the quinone methides in solution, for example, in acetone, is important. Decoloration owing to polymerization occurs with increasing rapidity in the series (*61*), (*62*) and (*64*). This reaction produces polymeric benzyl aryl ethers e.g. (*65*) containing a phenolic hydrogen at one end and a benzyl hydroxyl group at the other. The products are colorless or pale brown amorphous powders with degrees of polymerization of about 15 to 40. No attempts were made to achieve higher degrees of polymerization. It is quite possible that the quinone methide (*34*) also forms a polymerization product (*53*) and that such products, consisting of a few units, may exist in lignin (p. 92).

On treatment with hydrogen chloride, the polymers are rapidly degraded to monomolecular *p*-hydroxybenzyl chlorides, which then condense to red-brown irreversible polymers of type (*66*).

Both the *p*-hydroxybenzyl aryl ethers and the *p*-alkoxybenzyl aryl ethers are split at room temperature by methanol containing 0.5% HCl. The corresponding benzyl methyl ethers are formed together with free phenolic groups.

The *p*-hydroxybenzyl aryl ethers exhibit an interesting behaviour during the titration with sodium aminoethoxide in ethylene diamine mentioned on p. 71 (Fr. and Werner, 1964; Fr., Harkin and Werner, 1964). As soon as the terminal phenolic group has reacted, the next phenolic group is released from its benzyl aryl ether bond and is also titrated. Thus, simple *p*-hydroxybenzyl aryl ethers neutralize two equivalents of sodium aminoethoxide, and the polymers are completely degraded stepwise and titrated like monomeric phenols. The *p*-hydroxybenzyl aminoethyl ethers, which are probably formed in this reaction, have not been examined.

If the terminal *p*-hydroxyl groups are methylated with diazomethane, the resultant *p*-methoxybenzyl aryl ethers are no longer attacked by sodium aminoethoxide. The same applies to polymers that have been treated with diazomethane. This shows that they have a terminal phenolic group which reacts with the diazomethane.

This explains why the trilignol (*51*) and tetralignol (*52*) each require two equivalents of sodium aminoethoxide and why the hexalignol (*56*) neutralizes three equivalents.

The small amount of *p*-hydroxybenzyl aryl ethers in lignin (less than 0.05 per unit, perhaps 0.03) require two equivalents and are titrated together with the free phenolic groups (0.32 per unit). The content of *p*-alkoxybenzyl aryl ethers in lignin is slightly higher (perhaps 0.08) but is not revealed by this simple titration. Compound (*55*), for example, requires only one equivalent of sodium aminoethoxide.

During the isolation of the trilignol (*51*) and the tetralignol (*52*), difficulties were already encountered because of the ease of hydrolysis of the compounds. *p*-Hydroxybenzyl aryl ethers are rapidly hydrolysed by lukewarm water, and *p*-alkoxybenzyl aryl ethers are split within a week by water at 100 °C. The same hydrolysis occurs, although much more slowly, with the numerous guaiacylglycerol-β-aryl ethers of type (*35*) in lignin. Here a phenol and guaiacylglycerol (*67*) and (*70*) are formed. The latter is produced by prolonged hydrolysis of spruce wood by water at 100 °C in addition to other products and exists in two stereoisomeric forms (Nimz, 1966 a). These are the racemoid and mesoid (*67* to *70*) forms* and have also been prepared synthetically (Adler and Gustafson, 1963).

The ether-type linkages between carbohydrates and lignin mentioned above, for example, (*57*), are hydrolysed by acid in the case of free *p*-hydroxybenzyl sugar ethers at about the same rate as or faster than sucrose. During the hydrolysis of wood with water at 100 °C, the pH of the solution rapidly becomes 6.0 to 6.5; this acidity ought to suffice at that temperature to gradually cleave the lignin carbohydrate ethers. The influence of etherification of the *p*-hydroxyl group on the rate of hydrolysis has not yet been studied.

Exhaustive percolation of wood with water at 100 °C dissolves part of the lignin and the hemicelluloses. Spruce wood releases about 20% and beechwood about 40% of its dry weight into solution. The extract contains lignin and carbohydrate fractions in about the same proportions as they occur in the wood. The solubilized material includes sugars, lignols and probably lignol and lignin compounds with

* The proposal to designate such diastereoisomers racemoid and mesoid (K. Freudenberg: Stereochemie, S. Deuticke Verlag, Wien 1933, p. 686) has the advantage of being clearly intelligible and concise. Such isomers were later designated as *threo*- and *erythro*-forms. This configurational relationship to threose and erythrose entails the inconvenience that the reader must have the correct absolute configurations of these two tetroses in mind in order to visualize the correct structures of the isomers (cf. pinoresinol, p. 87). Combined with the modern designation, racemoid (RR, SS) and mesoid (RS) cover a much wider range than erythro and threo, which are more or less closely associated the with hydroxyl compounds.

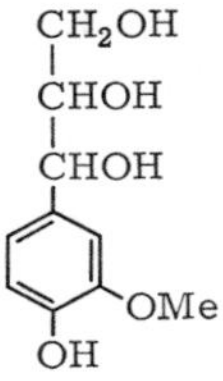

(67), (68) Guaiacylglycerol (diastereomer)

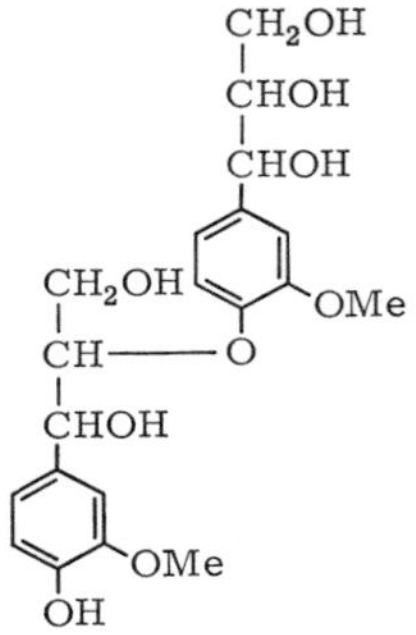

(69), (70) Guaiacylglycerol-β-guaiacylglycerol ether (diastereomer)

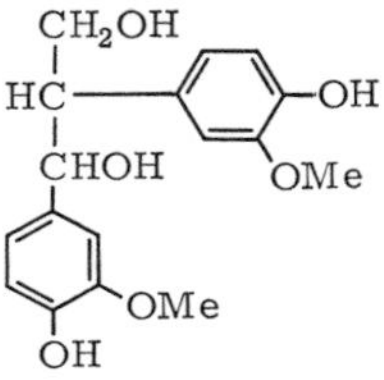

(44), (71) 1,2-Guaiacylpropan-1,3-diol (diastereomer)

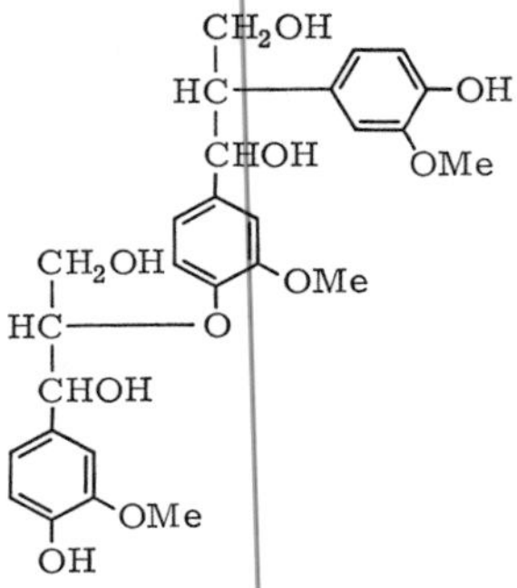

(72) β-Guaiacylglycerol ether of *(44, 71)*

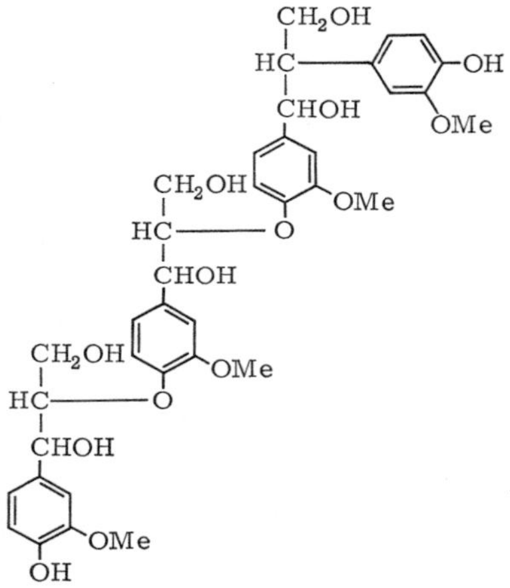

(73) β-Guaiacylglycerol ether of *(72)*

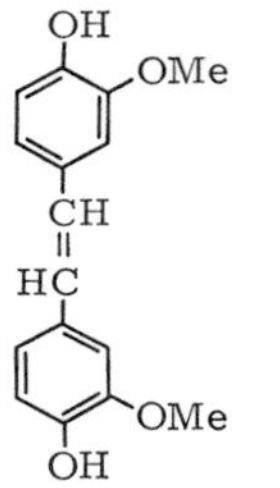

(74) 3,3'-Dimethoxy-4,4'-dihydroxystilbene

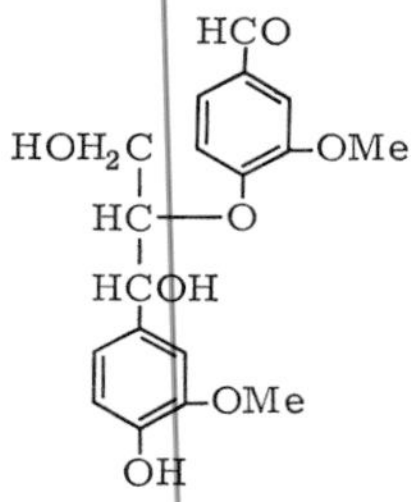

(74 a) Guaiacylglycerol-β-vanillyl ether

sugars. This release was previously studied by SCHÜTZ (1943); SCHÜTZ, SARTEN and MEYER (1948) who was unable to explain it correctly. He did not conceive of water-soluble lignin fragments and water-soluble lignin-carbohydrate complexes and so was led to an erroneous concept of the nature of lignin (p. 56, 59).

It is the hydrolysis of the lignin fraction that is of interest to us here (FR. and NIMZ, 1966; FR. et al., 1965; NIMZ, 1965, 1966, 1966 a, b, 1967; NIMZ and GABER 1965). When the water used for extraction at 100 °C does not become more acidic than pH 6 (when measured in the cold), no acid-catalysed condensations of the hydrolysis products appear to occur. The following substances have so far been obtained in very minute amounts from sprucewood: guaiacylglycerol (*67*) and (*68*), guaiacylglycerol-β-guaiacylglycerol ether (*69*, *70*), 1,2-diguaiacylpropane-1,3-diol (*44*, *71*) in its mesoid and racemoid forms (cf. p. 95, footnote), two of the eight possible racemates (*72*) of the guaiacylglycerol-β-ether of the diols (*44*, *71*), and the guaiacylglycerol-β-ether of this compound, the tetralignol (*73*) and guaiacylglycerol-β-vanillyl ether (*74a*). In addition, guaiacylglycerol-β-coniferyl ether (*35*) and its aldehyde (*36*) have been obtained from wood by heating with water or very dilute acetic acid (H. NIMZ, 1967 a). At room temperature, methanol containing 0.5% HCl splits off dehydrodiconiferyl alcohol (*30*) and DL-pinoresinol (*32*) (p. 86, 87). Cleavage products from beech lignin are described later.

It is noteworthy that guaiacylglycerol, (*67*) and (*68*), has never been encountered among the intermediates of dehydrogenation of coniferyl alcohol although it has been carefully sought. This is understandable, for it should not be formed by this reaction. Its presence in the lignin hydrolysis products is doubtless due to cleavage of lignols of the type of guaiacylglycerol-β-coniferyl ether (*35*). This dilignol is produced both during the dehydrogenation of coniferyl alcohol and during the hydrolysis of spruce lignin. In the same way as guaiacylglycerol, substances (*69*), (*70*) are formed by hydrolysis of products such as (*49*) or (*73*).

While the diguaiacylpropane-1,3-diols were found among the products of hydrolysis of spruce lignin, they appeared to be absent from the mixture of intermediates of dehydrogenation of coniferyl alcohol. However, after their properties had become known from the samples isolated by hydrolysis of spruce lignin, an explanation for this was found (FR. and NIMZ, 1966). During the chromatographic separation of the oligolignols, the spots for the diols (*44*) and (*71*) are masked by guaiacylglycerol-β-coniferyl ether (*35*) and have so far not been separated from it. Nonetheless, they are present (p. 91) and can be detected in mixtures by their transformation with hot alkali into the characteristic strongly fluorescent compound 4,4′-dihydroxy-3,3′-dimethoxystilbene (*74*) with simultaneous loss of formaldehyde and water.

The observation that the degradation products (*44*) or (*71*) obtained from lignin also occur among the intermediates of lignin synthesis in the laboratory is yet another assurance that the course of lignification is the same both *in vitro* and *in vivo*.

The formation of (*44*) and (*71*) can be explained by interaction of the radicals R_b (*25*) and R_d (*27*), the side chain of R_d being eliminated. Water is then added onto the quinone methide group of R_b. The constitutions of the trilignol (*72*) and the tetralignol (*73*) were elucidated by routine methods (p. 85) and by alkaline degradation (2 *N* NaOH, 135 °C) which yields the stilbene (*74*).

As mentioned above, numerous oligolignols are obtained from lignin or wood by mild hydrolysis. They are, in spite of the small yield, very significant for the rôle of the biosynthetic lignols as conclusive intermediates for the formation of lignin. An explanation why the yield cannot be better is given on p. 105.

E. Biochemical and Tracer Experiments

1. Biochemical Experiments and Other Observations

In this section, a short discussion will be given of biochemical and labelling experiments which were aimed at either showing the significance of the phenolic glucosides of the *p*-hydroxycinnamyl alcohols as the starting point of lignification, or proving the identity of the course of lignification *in vivo* and *in vitro*, or providing direct contributions to the elucidation of the constitution of lignin.

In spruce and other conifers, during the vegetative period, the tissues contain high concentrations of coniferin in the region around the cambium. In the cambium of older trunks, the latter is accompanied by very small amounts of *p*-glucocoumaryl alcohol and syringin (glucosides of (*1 a*) and (*1 c*) FR. and HARKIN, 1963). The cambium of one- or two-year-old spruce shoots contains relatively more *p*-glucocoumaryl alcohol than older spruce trees (FR. and TORRES-SERRES, 1967), and correspondingly the methoxyl content of young spruce milled-wood lignin lies around 12 to 13% instead of having the full 15.6% of mature spruce milled-wood lignin (FR. and LEHMANN, 1963; FR. and TORRES-SERRES, 1967, p. 70, 113). Is this phenomenon related to phylo- and ontogenesis? (See S. M. MANSKAJA 1958).

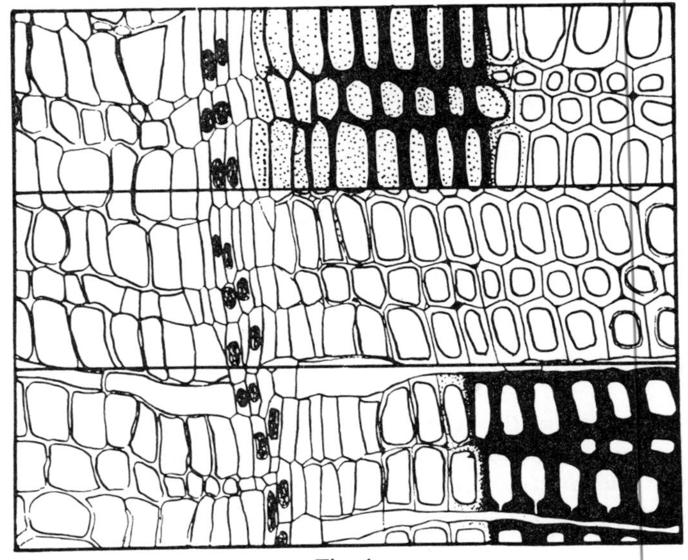

Fig. 1

Traces of free coniferyl alcohol can also be detected in the sap from cambial tissues of freshly felled trees. The low stationary concentration present is hardly sufficient to account for the profuse lignification going on. On the other hand, it is only the free phenolic alcohols and not their glucosides that can be transformed by the dehydrogenases into lignin. It was therefore suspected that a β-glucosidase must be present in the cambium tissues. However, attempts to detect a glucosidase in the cell sap were fruitless. It was therefore concluded that the enzyme must be firmly attached to the tissue; this proved to be the case.

The middle strip of the schematic Fig. 1 shows the intact cross section of young conifer shoots (FR. et al., 1952, 1954, 1955). The cambium cells are indicated by nuclei. The rows on the left of the cambium belong to the bark. On the right of the cambium are freshly produced not yet lignified cells. Further on the right, lignin is in production and from about the 9th row onwards lignification is finished.

If a similar cross-section of conifer shoot is moistened with a solution of phloroglucinol in hydrochloric acid, the following staining pattern is observed (FR. et al.,

1954, 1955), (Fig. 1, lowest part). In the region on the right side where the formation of wood is finished, the strong red color of lignified tissues appears. This lessens gradually and ceases at about the sixth to eighth row of cells inside the cambium.

In order to detect the β-glucosidase histologically, thin sections of the growing shoots were moistened with a solution of the glucoside indican*. If a β-glucosidase is present indican is split into indoxyl and glucose, and indoxyl is oxidized to indigo within a few minutes by the oxygen of the air. It was later called to our attention that BEIJERINCK (1900) had long before revealed the localisation of emulsin in sweet almonds by staining sections with the juice of dyer's woad (Isatis tinctoria), which contains indican.

In the upper part of Fig. 1 the indigo effect is visible starting at about the third or fourth layer of cells on the inside of the cambium ring and intensifying strongly up to the eight to tenth layers. Further inwards from about the eleventh to the twelfth layers, where the cell walls are thick and sturdy, the indigo effect stops abruptly. The mature wooded cell walls are physiologically dead.

Between the cambium and the wood the glucosides meet both the glucosidase and the dehydrogenases, which the *p*-hydroxycinnamic alcohols released by the glucosidase transform into lignin. Corresponding observations were made on the repeated clustered bundles of wooden tissue in the liliacea *Cordyline* (FR., KRAFT, and HEIMBERGER 1951; FR. et al., 1952).

There may be a simple connection between lignification and the timberline. The timberline on mountainsides or in the far north is a limit beyond which woody plants cannot grow in clusters to a height of more than 5 to 6 feet. G. SANDBERG (1960) has shown that in Lapland the limit of the birch forests is a function of the temperature. Above this limit the temperature is not high enough for regular lignification. The temperature coefficients of the various enzymes involved in lignification are not generally known. One or the other of these enzymes may be the limiting factor. It is known, however, that one of the β-glucosidases has a characteristically high temperature coefficient (DUERKSEN and HALVORSON, 1958).

2. Tracer Experiments

An indication that lignification in spruce is directly associated with a β-glucosidase is derived from repeated observations (FR. and BITTNER, 1953; KRATZL, BILLEK, KLEIN and BUCHTELA, 1957) that coniferin, labelled in the aglycon portion, when suitably administered to the plant, is incorporated irreversibly into its lignin. The radioactive lignin produced exhibits the characteristic properties of ordinary lignin on degradation, for example, the solubilities of milled-wood lignin or the production of radioactive vanillin or degradation acids when the label is diffuse. On the other hand, when a synthetic radioactive L-coniferin made from L-glucose is administered to the plant in exactly the same way as D-coniferin (FR. et al., 1954, 1955), it spreads out throughout the plant and can afterwards be reextracted with water; it is not converted into radioactive lignin.

* This compound has been synthesized by a modification of the procedure of A. ROBERTSON (1900). The method had to be revised owing to a printing error (FR. et al., 1952).

The experiments suggest that the major proportion, if not all the lignin monolignols, pass through the glucosidic form of the *p*-hydroxycinnamyl alcohols. To test this, cambial sap from spruce trunks was examined during the vegetative period (FR. and HARKIN, 1963). The freshly felled trees were cut into three-foot sections and immediately debarked and washed down with hot formaldehyde solution, the cambial tissues being scraped off during this process. In this way the enzymes are immediately inactivated. The solution contains the sap from the cambium and the adjacent layers of newly formed cells. Besides carbohydrates the main soluble component of the solution is coniferin, which is accompanied by small amounts of glucocoumaryl alcohol and syringin, which were identified after crystallisation. Phenolic compounds were also found in amounts that were so small that they could only be identified by chromatography. These included coniferyl alcohol, coniferaldehyde, dehydrodiconiferyl alcohol (*30*), pinoresinol (*32*), guaiacylglycerol-β-coniferyl ether (*35*), and guaiacylglycerol-β-pinoresinol ether (*47*). These substances can therefore be regarded as natural products. From the standpoint of their relative abundance they are also the most important intermediates for formation of artificial lignin. There are other phenolic compounds in the cambial sap, but, with the exception of hydroxy-matairesinol (*42*), which is easy to recognise (FR. and KNOF, 1957), they are hard to identify unequivocally because of their low concentration and the complexity of the mixture.

It is known from numerous experiments by our own and other teams that various C_6C_3 acids are good lignin precursors. Phenylalanine (cf. A. C. NEISH, preceding article) plays a prominent rôle among these, and has the advantage of being available in several specifically labelled forms. If DL-phenylalanine-$^{14}CHNH_2$ is administered to young spruce twigs by infusion (FR. and LEHMANN, 1963), part of the radioactivity is incorporated within a few weeks into lignin in the few rows of cells which were in the process of lignification when the application was made. On the other hand, if the experiment is interrupted a few days after the infusion of the tracer, the β-glucosides of the three *p*-hydroxycinnamyl alcohols can be isolated in a radioactive yield around 0.03% (FR. and TORRES-SERRES, 1967; FR., 1965 b; FR. et al., 1969).

The calculation of this yield bases on the total activity of the phenylalanine infused in the twigs. After application, a seventh of the radioactivity has been encountered in the water-soluble extract. Under this aspect 0.2% of the radioactivity can be retraced in the glucosides after application of L-phenylalanine-$^{14}CO_2H$.

An experiment aimed at testing the identity of artificial and natural lignin was made, starting from β-labelled coniferyl alcohol. The radioactive coniferyl alcohol was transformed in the laboratory into its dehydrogenation product (DHP). This product was then degraded by oxidation after methylation and the veratric, isohemipinic and metahemipinic acids were isolated. The specific radioactivities of the three acids relative to that of the DHP were in the ratios 1%:50.5%:10.5% (FR., JONES and RENNER, 1963; FR. et al., 1965). "β" means the middle position, p. 55.

The same degradation was applied to the wood of young spruce harvested in August into which the [β-^{14}C] coniferin had been introduced in June. The specific activities of the same three acids, based on that of the radioactive wood, were within the limits of error in the same ratios as in the experiment with coniferyl alcohol *in vitro* namely 53% for isohemipinic and 12% for metahemipinic acid (FR. et al., 1965).

The weak but unmistakable radioactivity of the veratric acid may be due to the occurrence of diguaiacylpropanediol units (*44*) and (*71*) in lignin, which yield a molecule of active and a molecule of inactive veratric acid with the labelling used in this experiment.

The 50% relative activity of the isohemipinic acid indicates that the radioactive half of the acid obtained includes the isohemipinic acid derived from dehydrodiconiferyl alcohol residues (*30*) in lignin, while the inactive half is probably derived from biphenyl or other structures. The active portion of the small amount of metahemipinic acid can perhaps be explained by a product formed by interaction of R_b (*25*) with R_d (*27*) followed by a dienone-phenol rearrangement. Alternatively, because of the multitude of free radicals involved in lignification, it is conceivable that some radical exchange reactions can occur that lead to dehydrogenation of the 6-position of a coniferyl alcohol unit, leading to a free radical in that position, which then combines with an R_b radical.

Regardless of the interpretation of the radioactivities of these three acids II, IV (*8*) and V (*9*) (p. 79), the experiments with β-labelled starting materials prove that the analogy between artificial and natural lignification holds true even on a quantitative basis.

The experiment with β-labelled coniferyl alcohol and coniferin has been extended on phenylalanine ($^{14}CHNH_2$) and on α-, β- and γ-labelled substances (Fr., Lehmann, 1963; Fr. and Swaleh, 1969; Fr., Toribio, Penzien and Garg, 1969). The results are enumerated in Table 3.

Table 3

Substance used for degradation	Products of the degradation	Labelling in the side chain		
		terminal	middle	ring adjacent
Dehydrogenation product (DHP) from lab. coniferyl alcohol	Formaldehyde	active		
	Veratric acid	activity ca. 1%	activity ca. 1%	activity 90%
	Isohemipinic acid	activity ca. 1%	activity 50.5%	activity 90%
	Metahemipinic ac.		activity 10.5%	
Spruce wood lign. after application of lab. coniferin	Formaldehyde	active		
	Veratric ac.	activity ca. 1%		
	Isohemipinic ac.		activ. 53% of lign.	
	Metahemipinic ac.		activ. 12% of lign.	
Spruce wood lign. after application of lab. DL-phenylalanine	Formaldehyde	active		
	Veratric acid	act. 2% of lign.	act. 1% of lign.	
	Isohemipinic acid	act. 7% of lign.	act. 29% of lign.	
	Metahemipinic acid		act. 15% of lign.	
	Hemipinic acid		act. 10% of lign.	

Illustration of Table 3

Percent activity refers to the substance enumerated in the first vertical column. The results with iso- and m-hemipinic acids (labelling of the middle C atom) are already explained just above. The experiment with phenylalanine gave less exact results than coniferin. It must be remembered that the behaviour in the plant of the D-antipode of DL-phenylalanine is uncertain. The results of labelling the middle C atoms stress the conclusion that there is a shorter and more direct way from coniferin to lignin than from phenylalanine, which causes randomization.

Vanillin which had been substituted with deuterium in the 5-, 6-, or 2-position was used to synthesize the correspondingly deuterated coniferyl alcohol molecules. Details are given on p. 108. When dehydrogenation products were prepared from these coniferyl alcohols, loss of deuterium occurred in each case: 45% from the 5-position, 8 to 10% from the 6-position, and 2 to 4% from the 2-position (Fr., Jovanovic and Topfmeier, 1961; Fr. and Jovanovic, 1963). The equivalent amounts of condensation in these positions have of course taken place during lignification:

It has been estimated by Pew (1962, 1963) that there are 25% or more units participating in biphenyl bonds in lignin; in addition there are about 10% of diphenyl ethers in which about 5% of the units are engaged in position 5. These and the involvement of the 5-position (7%) in dehydrodiconiferyl alcohol (*30*) account for most of the condensations through C—5. In addition, an unknown number of condensations occur at C—5 owing to rearrangements of benzyl aryl ether leading to C—γ to C—5 bonds [cf. unit 2 in (*75*)]. In lignin, therefore, about 40% of the units are involved in 5-position, in accordance with the experiment using deuterium.

The 6-position can be substituted as mentioned above by radical interchange or scattering as well as by dienonephenol rearrangements. The degradation acids (*12*) and (*9*) (p. 79) could be the products of such reactions. The 6-position can also be involved in rearrangements of the benzyl aryl ethers. These observations correspond with the loss of deuterium from the 6-position. It is only 20 to 25% of the amount lost from the 5-position.

F. Schematic Model of the Constitution of Spruce Lignin

In order to construct a schematic constitution of spruce lignin and taking for granted the parallelism of natural and artificial lignin formation, several authors have more or less arbitrarily combined some of the above described oligolignols to larger aggregates. Such attempts depended upon the kind and the number of intermediates known at that moment, and need control as shown on p. 73 and 105 f.

It is self-evident that a schematic constitution can only include a small part of the 100 or more units present in a lignin particle. The scheme depicted in (*75*) is a fragment made up of 18 units (plus six variants) interlinked in a fashion corresponding to the biochemical growth of the naturally occurring lignin molecule.

Apart from this biogenetic aspect, which forms the major criterion in constructing the model, numerous other data from lignin chemistry are incorporated into the draft of the lignin formula shown in (*75*). These data include the elemental composition of spruce lignin, the number and type of hydroxyl and ether groups (p. 73), the mutual ratios of the three basic alcohols (*1a* to *1c*), the carbonyl group content, the amount of the three most important dilignols (*30, 32, 35*), the condensations due to rearrangements of guaiacylglycerol-γ-aryl ethers [type (*67*)], and some structural elements inferred from the methoxylated acids obtained by degradation.

An attempt to build up a lignin formula automatically leads to a step-by-step construction, for example, of a hexalignol (units (U) 1 to 6) linked to a trilignol (U 7 to 9) to which a single unit (10) is attached. In this way a decalignol (U 1 to 10) is formed, which is dehydrogenated at its terminal phenolic group (U 10) to give an aroxyl radical. The aroxyl radical reacts with an R_b (*25*) radical (U 11) to give a terminal quinone methide grouping, which in turn adds another preformed polylignol such as the heptalignol (U 12 to 18). This illustrates how a single unit in its R_b form (U 11) is capable of binding a preformed decalignol and a heptalignol together to give an octadecalignol. Such a process doubtless also occurs in nature. Small and medium-sized aggregates are "glued" together by single R_b radicals to form larger entities. The sequence of the individual units in lignin is fortuitous, for they are not moulded like proteins on a template. This does not exclude occurrence of a certain regularity in the distribution of weak and strong bonds between the units. As a rough estimate, 7 to 9 weak bonds are randomly distributed among 100 units, "glueing" together more resistant clusters of, on an average, 14 units.

The activity of the enzymes is restricted to the dehydrogenation of the phenolic groups and is therefore sterically nonspecific. All the artificial lignols, the artificial and natural lignins, and the lignin degradation products are optically inactive.

In order to construct a lignin model, the mentioned oligolignols with 6 (U 1 to 6), 5 (U 7 to 11) and 7 (U 12 to 18) units are built up in the following manner, which exhibits, in an arbitrary sequence, the interlinking of the units, as they are established by the oligolignols (intermediates) and the acids obtained by degradation of lignin.

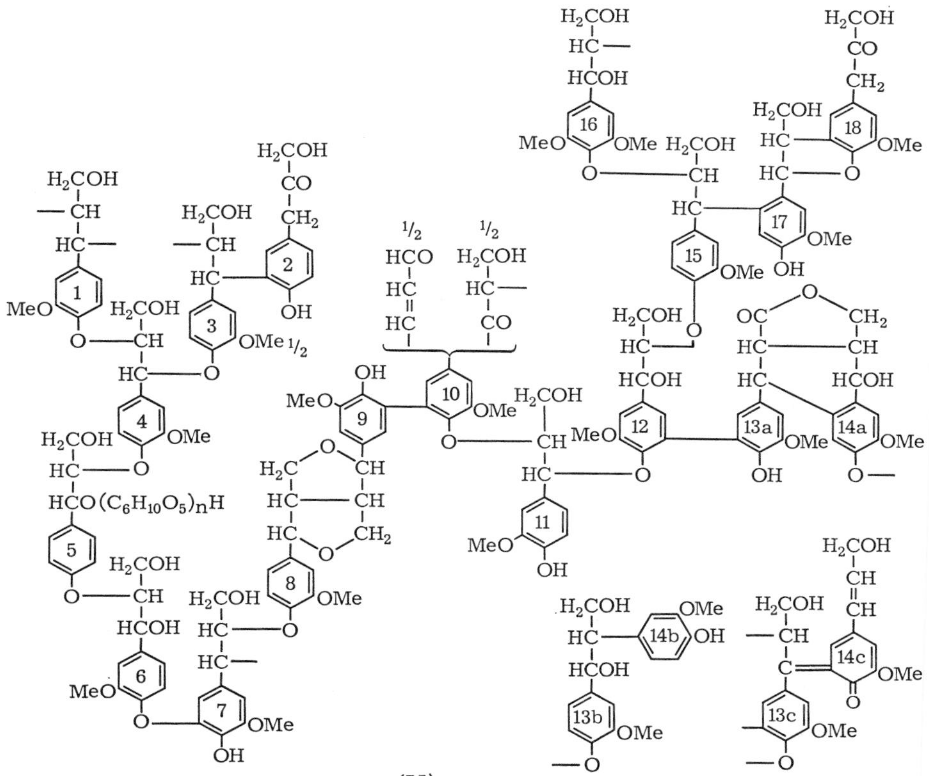

(*75*)

Unit 1 (U 1) is part of a guaiacylglycerol diaryl ether which has been dehydrogenated at the phenolic group. It combines with a radical R_b (U 4) which adds to its quinone methide group the preformed dilignol (U 2, U 3). (U 3) originates from a mixture of about one part of coniferyl alcohol and one part of *p*-coumaryl alcohol. This mixture is dehydrogenated and reacts in its R_b form with the R_d form (*24*) of (U 2) to give a benzylaryl ether. This ether (U 3, U 2) forms by rearrangement a diphenylmethane derivative. The side chain of (U 2) had originally the aspect of the side chain of (U 4). Due to summer temperature or for other reasons the benzylaryl ether group has lost the phenolic portion together with the β-H-atom to form an enol ether. This is easily hydrolyzed and leaves the side chain of (U 2) as a ketone. Now the tetralignol 1 to 4 is completed.

It is dehydrogenated at the phenolic group of (U 4) which reacts with (U 5) in its R_b form. This unit again belongs to the coumaryl group. Its quinone methide group adds on a polysaccharide to form a phenol. The phenol group of (U 5) is dehydrogenated and reacts with R_b (U 6), the quinone methide group of which combines with water.

Meanwhile a pinoresinol molecule (U 8 to U 9) in its R_a form has reacted in the well-known way with R_b (U 7) to which water or a phenol group (not depicted here) is attached. (U 7) is dehydrogenated and reacts in its R_b form. This combines with the R_a form of (U 6) to give a diphenyl ether. Now the nonolignol (U 1 to U 9) is formed. (U 10) is a mixture of coniferaldehyde and a guaiacyl ketone which has been formed by oxidation of a lignol similar to (U 12). Both (U 9) and (U 10) react with each other, after dehydrogenation, in their R_c (*26*) form. A decalignol 1 to 10 is now formed.

The decalignol is linked after dehydrogenation to the heptalignol 12 to 18 by interposition of R_b (U 11). Here (U 16) which was formerly a sinapyl alcohol molecule had reacted after dehydrogenation in its corresponding R_b form, simultaneously adding water. After being dehydrogenated again, it has combined with (U 15), which has reacted in its R_b form to add (U 16). (U 17) was added, with its phenol group, on U 15 when this was still a quinone methide, to form a benzyl aryl ether. This has undergone rearrangement in a similar way as (U 2). (U 17) and (U 18) were originally dehydrodi-coniferyl alcohol (*30*). The β-keto group of (U 18) has the same origin as that of (U 2).

The phenol group of (U 15) of the tetralignol (U 15 to U 18) has been dehydrogenated and has reacted with (U 12) in its R_b form. The product has added water and after dehydrogenation has reacted, in its R_c form, with the group (U 13 to 14).

(U 13a, b, c and 14a, b, c) represent units occurring to a very small extent in spruce lignin. (U 13a and 14a) correspond to the hypothetical cyclolignane (*41*) which is expected to be formed very easily from the intermediate lignenolide (*40*). (U 13b and 14b) belong to the group of 1,2-diguaiacyl-propane-1,3-diols (*44*) encountered in spruce lignin as well as in artificial lignin. (U 13c to 14c) represents a quinoid grouping which is very probable in spruce lignin and originates from a diphenyl methane derivative as represented by the (U 2 and 3) (FR. and HARKIN, 1964).

The construction has proceeded now to the lignols (U 1 to U 10) and (*U* 12 to U 18). The former is dehydrogenated and adds on (U 11) in its R_b form on which again (U 12) is added to form a benzyl aryl ether bond. *U 11 is a linking unit which unites preformed oligolignols to larger aggregates and can release them again easily.*

This conception, combined with the notion of an extension on a surface (p. 93) hindering conglobulation makes it understandable how the lignin aggregate can grow to large dimensions (FR. 1962, 1965 and later papers).

G. Appraisal of the Schematic Formula for Spruce Lignin

When comparing the schematic constitution of lignin with the analytical data, we have to distinguish between such data which were *a priori* incorporated into the scheme and others which were not taken into consideration when constructing the scheme. Exact coincidence cannot be expected because, in many cases, the number of units chosen for the construction is too small.

Considering the first group of data, we must ask whether such a scheme can reproduce approximately the facts which were incorporated into the scheme when it was constructed. The scheme is built up from 161 carbon atoms (without methoxyl groups). When reducing a number (for example, the total number of the hydroxyl or methoxyl groups) to the C_9 unit, we have to multiply by 9/161 = 0.056. The elementary composition calculated from the formula is $C_9H_{7.02}O_2[H_2O]_{0.4}$ $[OCH_3]_{0.92}$. It is in agreement with the average analysis of spruce lignin given previously (p. 69). The loss of hydrogen atoms compared with the original *p*-hydroxycinnamic alcohols is $10 - 0.92 - 7.02 = 2.06$. The proportion of *p*-coumaryl alcohol to coniferyl alcohol to sinapyl alcohol in the schematic formula is 13.9:80.6:5.5. For these calculations the saccharide group attached to unit 5 is replaced by an H-atom.

The oxygen balance has already been reported on p. 73. The numbers in brackets were calculated from this scheme. The schematic formula is adapted as closely as possible to the analytical data for oxygen distribution. On the other hand the formula has been developed primarily by considering the rules of lignin formation as disclosed by studies on the synthesis and degradation of lignin. It is noteworthy that it has been possible to obtain good agreement between observed and calculated values for oxygen distribution and for much other information which was incorporated intentionally, e.g. the number and type of carbonyl groups. Other data from lignin chemistry incorporated into the draft are the amount of the three most important dilignols (*30*), (*32*) and (*35*). The dilignol (*30*) is originally represented by (U 17 and 18). One molecule of pinoresinol (*32*) is found in the combination of (U 8 and 9). This means that 11% of each of these two dilignols are represented in the scheme, whereas the skeleton of guaiacylglycerol-β-coniferyl ether (*35*) is used to a much larger extent in the construction. Probably the dehydrodiconiferyl alcohol (*30*) and pinoresinol (*32*) should be represented to a larger extent in a scheme built up from more than 18 units.

Among the host of ether bonds occuring in lignin, the benzyl aryl ethers are hydrolysed with the highest rate. Their number is low since only about 16% of the units participate in such bonds. In the schematic model they are represented by (U 3 to 4 and U 11 to 12). Oligolignols with a small number of units can only be split off if they are located in the periphery (as dilignol 2.3) or if an oligolignol is, by chance, combined by such weak bonds on both ends with other units. This is the reason why the yield of oligolignols obtained by mild hydrolysis is very low (p. 97).

The number of units (22%) involved in biphenyl bonds (p. 108) may also be too few (p. 102). This kind of bond — not their amount — was used intentionally for the construction of the scheme. The number of these bonds is indicated in Table 2.

A fundamental premise for constructing the formula was the use of the C_6C_3 units, with the single exception of (U 14 b). Both the use of C_6C_3 units and this exception have been discussed above (p. 65). The number of condensations of the type shown between (U 15 and 17) is undoubtedly exaggerated in the scheme. This type occurs to a far smaller extent than the type of condensation shown between (U 3 and 2). Structures such as that formed by (U 2 and 3) are readily dehydrogenated to give colored quinonoid products; these could explain part of the carbonyl content of lignin (U 14 c).

We can conclude, therefore, that it has been possible by such a scheme to express in a reasonable way the facts enumerated above which were incorporated intentionally in constructing the scheme. This is the first statement.

More important is the second question to be addressed to the scheme. Is it able to explain the great number of facts which were not incorporated during its construction? One fact which could not be predicted was that using rigid rules a satisfactory construction is possible. The sequence of the individual units in lignin is fortuitous. Nevertheless their interaction is regulated by strict rules which are imposed by the nature of the building stones and the mechanism of biochemical phenol dehydrogenation. The analytical study of lignin is complicated by the fact that the *p*-hydroxycinnamyl alcohols are combined in very different individual forms. When examining the scheme, it is found that only 2 of the 18 units + 6 variations are identical with each other; they are (U 1 and 4). All others differ from each other. It was unexpected and quite surprising that this fact is expressed to such an extent by the scheme. Another observation has already been mentioned: that a lignin molecule can only be depicted when preformed oligolignols combine to larger aggregates. This has long been observed in preparing artificial lignin and is undoubtedly the mode in which lignin is formed in nature. This fact may cause certain regularities on a higher level than can be expressed with only 18 units.

Another fact represented by the scheme, more or less incidentally, is the large amount of branching in the molecule. We find branching in (U 3, 4, 11, 12 and 15). This means that more than one fourth of the units are involved in branching and, occasionally, formation of large rings. Peripheral units, with bonds to units not shown in the model, are not included in this figure. In any case the number is high and is in agreement with the observation that the diazobenzenesulfonic acid compound of lignin exhibits, in the spreading experiments on a mercury surface, the properties of a highly branched three dimensional substance (FR. and BRAUN, 1931) (p. 59).

The number of units that can react with thioglycolic acid is correctly represented in the scheme (Table 4); the same applies approximately to the reactions with sulphurous acid. These reactions have been differentiated by ERDTMAN (1940, 1940 a); LINDGREN (1952); MIKAWA, and others and have been surveyed by SARKANEN (1963) (Table 4).

Investigating the different stages of the sulfite process, these authors established reactive groups *X*, *Z*, and *B*. Their difference is due to free or etherified phenyl hydroxyl or benzylhydroxyl.

Group *X* = *p*-hydroxybenzyl alcohols, and
p-hydroxybenzyl alkyl ethers,
Z = *p*-alkoxybenzyl alcohols,
B = *p*-alkoxybenzyl alkyl ethers.

Table 4. *Comparison of reactions of lignin with predictions by the model presented*

	Found or estimated	Predicted from model
Units able to undergo thioglycolic acid reaction, i.e. γ-ether, γ-carbinol, phenylethylene, carbonyl (twice)	0.8	0.8
Lignosulfonic acid formation		
Group *X* } *A*	0.15	0.17
Group *Z* } *A*	0.15	0.20
Group *B*	0.30	0.28
sum	0.60	0.65
Uptake of methanol (0.5% HCl, 20 °C)	0.62	0.72
Same after treatment with $NaBH_4$	0.42	0.41

Since these investigations, the arylbenzyl ethers and diaryl ethers have been detected in lignin. It seems possible to replace in all cases "alkyl ethers" by "alkyl or aryl ethers" or simply by "ethers". Because of the slow reaction of phenylcoumarans, (U 17) is placed among group *B*. From this point of view, group *X* (Table 4) consists of (U 9 and 11) of the scheme. As soon as (U 11) has reacted, (U 12) acquires also the structure of this group. Group *Z* may consist of (U 6, 14 a, 13 b, and 16); the ethylene groups of (U 10/2 and 14 c) may also be placed in group *Z*. (U 1, 4, 5, 8, and 17) may belong to *B*. The carbonyl groups are not taken into consideration because of the lability of their SO_2 adducts. The subdivision into *X*, *Z*, and *B* is uncertain. More significant is the sum of *X*, *Z*, and *B* which is found to be 0.60 per unit, whereas calculation from the scheme gives 0.65.

A lignin fragment like (*75*) would be split with sulfite preferentially between (U 3 to 4) and (U 11 to 12). The degradation product (U 2 and 3) would not react with sulfite, the heptalignol (U 12 to 18) would react with three molecules and the nonalignol (U 1 and 4 to 11) with eight molecules to give acids with 3 and 8 sulfo groups, respectively. These reactions in the γ position would be followed by the degradation of the β-ether bonds and the opening of the hydrofurane (U 17 to 18). Such a line of reasoning is only admissible if the γ-ethers are not condensed by the acid during the reaction with sulfite. This question is still open. If no condensation does occur, lignin of a schematic formula (*75*), when extended to 100 units, would give about 10 degradation products containing, on average over a wide range, 10 units each. 90 sulfonic groups would be distributed over the 10 fragments.

The reactivity of lignin with methanol containing 0.5% HCl has been studied quantitatively by E. Adler and Gierer (1957).

In Table 5 a comparison of other lignin reactions which were not incorporated into the model is presented.

Table 5. *Further comparison of lignin reactions with predictions from the model*

Characteristics		Finding or estimate	Model prediction
Condensations at C-5		0.45	0.42
Condensations at C-6		0.08	0.07
Condensations at C-2		0.04	
Units participating in biphenyl bonds		0.25 to 0.30 (PEW 1962/3)	0.22
Units able to form Hibbert ketones		0.1	0.17
Units able to form vanillin and vanillic acid		0.32	0.30 to 0.35
Aromatic and similar protons	by N.M.R. spectra	2.5	2.4
Aliphatic protons	by N.M.R. spectra	3.8	3.8

Using coniferyl alcohol substituted by deuterium in positions either C-5, 6, or 2, corresponding artificial DHPs were prepared in water as well in nearly pure D_2O (FR., JOVANOVIĆ and TOPFMEIER, 1961; FR. and JOVANOVIĆ, 1963, see p. 102). In water somewhat lower D contents were obtained. The average value was regarded as the true one. It is indicated in Table 5. The comparison between model and experiment with lignin needs a correction since in the latter a sinapyl unit was used. The amount of substitution shown at C-5 in the model was not adjusted intentionally; the quantitative agreement is remarkable. The model does not show substitution at C-2 because of the small number (18 units) used for building the model. The amount of C-6 substitution shown is chiefly intentional.

Biphenylyl bonds participate in 4 units of the scheme (U 9 to 10, 12 to 13a and 13c) and the minute amount of 5-6-diphenylyl bond.

Hibbert ketones (p. 63, 77, 78) can result from all coniferyl units which are not condensed in the C_6C_3 system (U 1, 4, 11), and vanillin from coniferyl units not condensed in the benzene nucleus.

In N.M.R. spectroscopy (Table 5) the evaluation both of the experiment (LUDWIG, NIST and MCCARTHY, 1964) and the model is in good agreement.

A formula containing only 18 units and representing a fraction of a lignin molecule can be regarded only as an approximation, no matter how good. That is why some alternative units have been included beside the main chain: these alternatives have been taken into account in making the calculations previously given.

Thus, there appears to be no well established fact regarding lignin that cannot be explained by reference to the scheme which is obviously realistic.

H. Other Proposals for Formulae

During the last decade several attempts have been made to establish parts of a lignin formula by combining some of the then known or surmised biosynthetic oligolignols and degradation products. The more detailed constitution formula (*75*) has been compared with lignin as described above. A formula presented by Ludwig, Nist and McCarthy (1964) consists of 10 C_9 units combined to a large ring. It has been built up with the intention to demonstrate the number of aromatic and aliphatic H atoms in coniferous lignin as determined by NMR spectroscopy. The number of 10 units for the ring has been chosen at random. The kind and distribution of the H atoms are in agreement with spruce lignin and the schematic formula (*75*) (Table 5). The formula (*75*) offers various possibilities for ring formation of different size.

A group of the Finnish Pulp and Paper Research Institute (Forss and Fremer 1964, 1965; Forss, Fremer and Stenlund, 1966; Jensen et al., 1966; Fogelberg et al., 1967) fractionated spent sulphite liquor from unextracted spruce with Sephadex. 10 to 20% of the material was of low molecular weight and was removed. Of the remaining acids, a part containing 30 to 40% of the lignin (Fig. 11, Forss, Fremer and Stenlund, 1966) was fractionated; the rest with higher molecular weight was also rejected. The fractions investigated were, according to the authors, composed of 10 to 18 lignin units, and equally contained 8 SO_3H groups. Based on this experiment the authors built up a detailed constitutional formula of lignin. They suggest a "repeating unit" consisting of 18 C_9 entities each and exhibiting a regular sequence throughout the lignin. It is necessary to compare their formula with the analytical data for spruce lignin. In the following, to avoid confusion, the C_9 entity is called "unit" and Forss' "repeating unit", which contains 18 C_9 entities, may be called "repeating aggregate". The comparison is based on Fig. 1 in the paper of Forss et al. p. 676 (1966).

Table 6. *Comparison of Forss' formula with spruce lignin, prepared following* Björkman

	Forss	Spruce
Elementary composition	$C_9H_{8.66}O_{2.89}[OCH_3]_{0.89}$	$C_9H_{7.95}O_{2.4}[OCH_3]_{0.92}$
hydroxyl groups in 100 units (without 22 OH groups etherified with carbohydrates)	167	133 no carbohydrates present
units containing hydroxyls in β-position	44%	not detected
secondary hydroxyls in 100 units	67	25
units containing phenolic groups	22%	32%
units participating in benzyl aryl ethers, non-cyclic	89%	16%
units participating in non-cyclic aliphatic ethers	22%	not detected
units participating in diphenyl ethers	absent	11%
content of dehydro-di-coniferyl alcohol derivatives	absent	11% or more
content of pinoresinol derivatives	absent	11% or more

The aliphatic α-α ether bonds (22% of the units) connecting, according to FORSS, the "repeating" aggregates would be, in contradiction to FORSS' opinion, the most stable of all. Such bonds have not yet been detected in lignin. The weakest bonds between lignin units are the non-cyclic benzylaryl ethers (89% of the units according to FORSS). Compared with spruce lignin, a lignin following FORSS contains 5 to 6 times more of this kind of bonding. The regularity claimed by FORSS for the sulfonic acid fractions needs further analytical proof, for instance the analysis of free sulfonic acids (cf. p. 54). His proposal of a new name for the fractions of low molecular weight is not necessary. PEARL (1967, p. 129) places, tentatively, milled wood lignin into this group. Its polymerisation degree, however, is about 50.

Although FORSS et al. stress the point that their draft does not represent any final formula, they cannot, nevertheless, propose formulae which differ fundamentally from the analytical data of spruce lignin. Forss' experimental results cannot be taken into consideration for the constitution of lignin. This has recently been explained in detail (FR. 1968).

It is a long way from the investigation of spent sulphite liquor to a lignin formula. The constitutional chemistry of lignin needs other tools than Sephadex and waste sulphite liquor. The latter needs investigation, indeed, as it is not yet clear whether it is an artefact or not.

Whereas FORSS claims a regular distribution of the units in lignin, the investigation of lignin itself, its degradation and biosynthesis can only be explained by an irregular sequence.

On the other hand, a lignin of a constitution similar to scheme (*75*) would give results not far from those claimed by FORSS (p. 93, 104, 107). There is no reason for making an alteration of scheme (*75*) in which each kind and even—as far as possible—each quantity of bonding is based on experimental facts.

I. Beech Lignin, Other Kinds of Lignin and the Concept of Lignin; Lignite and Humic Acid

1. Beech Lignin and Other Kinds of Lignin

Whereas the derivatives of pyrogallol are very scant in spruce wood lignin, in beechwood tar they are present in abundance, in addition to the allied catechol derivatives. Like all hardwoods, beechwood yields on degradation with nitrobenzene and alkali, more syringaldehyde than vanillin. Very little *p*-hydroxybenzaldehyde is produced. A 9:1 v/v mixture of acetone and water extracts from powdered beechwood at room temperature only extremely small amounts of gummy materials containing traces of ferulic acid and 2,6-dimethoxy-*p*-benzoquinone. Beech lignin contains almost 22% methoxyl, or about one-and-a-half times as much methoxyl as spruce lignin. The average composition of 2 milled wood lignin preparations (FR. and SIDHU, 1961 a; FR. and HARKIN, 1964) from beech (Fagus sylvatica) is $C_9H_{6.43}O_2[H_2O]_{0.53}[OCH_3]_{1.30}$. The composition of the mixture of the three cinnamyl alcohols from which beech lignin is produced has tentatively the molar proportions

53% coniferyl alcohol, 4% *p*-coumaryl alcohol and 43% sinapyl alcohol. The composition of such a mixture is $C_9H_{8.61}O_2[OCH_3]_{1.39}$; beech lignin contains 2.2 H-atoms less and 0.53 mole of water more.

On prolonged extraction water at 100 °C removes 40% of the total weight of beechwood. About 8.8% of the extract is material that is derived from its lignin (40% of the beech lignin). The following substances have been isolated from this fraction:

Di-O-methyl-pyrogallylglycerol (*76*), (Fr. et al., 1965; Nimz, 1965 a),
DL-syringaresinol (*77*) (Nimz and Gaber, 1965) (cf. p. 96),
1,2-di-guaiacyl-propane-1,3-diol (*44*), (*69*) (Nimz, 1966 a),
1-guaiacyl-2-di-O-methyl-pyrogallyl-propane-1,3-diol (*78*) (Nimz, 1966 a),
1,2-bis-di-O-methyl-pyrogallyl-propane-1,3-diol (*79*) (Fr. et al., 1965; Nimz, 1965 a, 1965 b, 1966 b; survey: Nimz, 1966).

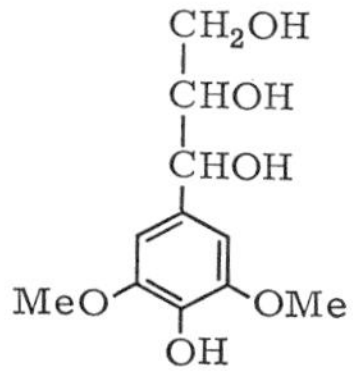

(*76*) (Di-O-methyl-pyrogallyl)-glycerol

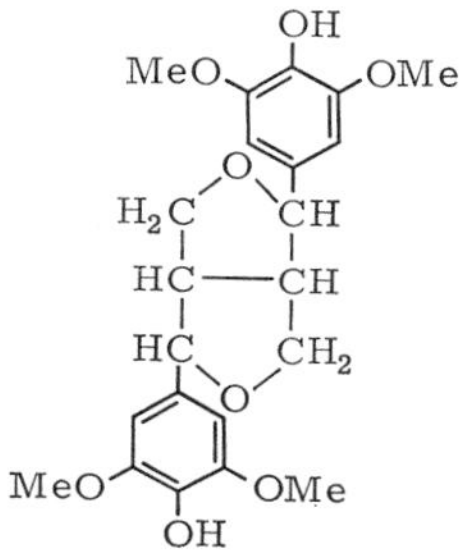

(*77*) Syringa-resinol

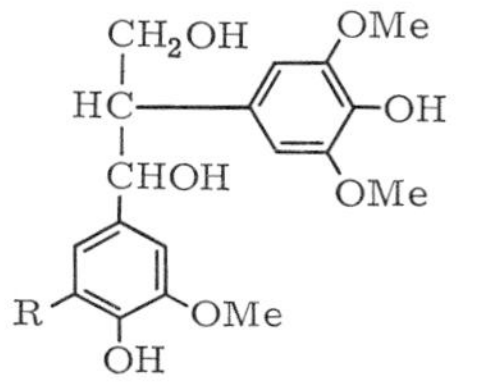

(*78*) R=H, 1-Guaiacyl-2-dimethylpyro-gallyl-propandiol
(*79*) R=OOH_3, Bis-di-methyl-pyrogallyl-propandiol

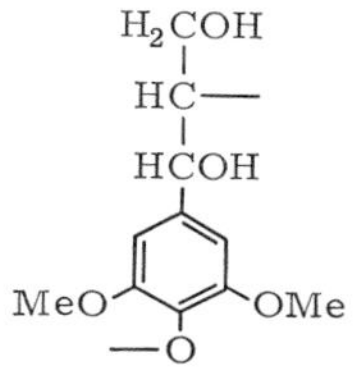

(*80*) Dehydrated unit (*76*)

DL-Syringaresinol is easily produced by dehydrogenation of sinapyl alcohol (Fr. and Bittner, 1950; Fr., Kraft and Heimberger, 1951; Fr. et al., 1958a). Continued dehydrogenation of this alcohol does not lead to a lignin-like polymer but instead to dimethoxy benzoquinone and other degradation products (Fr., Kraft and Heimberger, 1951; Fr. et al., 1958a; Fr. and Hübner, 1952).

However, if a 1:1 mixture of coniferyl alcohol and sinapyl alcohol is dehydrogenated, a lignin-like dehydrogenation product is formed (Fr. and Hübner, 1952). If the sinapyl alcohol component predominates in the mixture, the excess is not incorporated into the polymer (Fr., 1960, 1962). This is in accordance with the fact that no lignin has ever been found with a methoxyl content higher than that calculated for the 1:1 mixture of coniferyl and sinapyl alcohols (calc. 23.3% OCH_3).

When a molecular mixture of 5-deuteroconiferyl alcohol and sinapyl alcohol is dehydrogenated, the relative loss of deuterium is about the same as in the experiment with coniferyl alcohol alone, i.e. ca. 45% (Fr., Jovanović and Topfmeier, 1961; Fr. and Jovanović, 1963). Coniferyl alcohol, therefore, seems to act in like manner in the presence or absence of sinapyl alcohol. If the same is assumed with *p*-coumaryl alcohol, one can try to transform the model formula of spruce lignin (*15*) into one of beech lignin. In so doing, the 14.5 coniferyl units must remain unaltered; (U 5) has to be methoxylated in position 3.

If 12 units of dehydrogenated sinapyl alcohol are now incorporated, a model of 30 units with the following composition would result:

coumaryl units	1.5 =	5%
coniferyl units	15.5 =	52%
sinapyl units	13.0 =	43%
	30.0 .	

This raises the question of how the 12 units of dehydrogenated sinapyl alcohol would fit into the model. A radical corresponding to R_c *(26)* is excluded. An aroxyl radical [type R_a *(24)*] can occur to some extent. A radical corresponding to R_b *(25)* is doubtless most favored; this is proved by the easy formation of syringaresinol *(77)* and its occurrence as a hydrolysis product of beech lignin. Di-methylpyrogallyl-glycerol originates also from a R_b type radical. Also, a radical of the kind of R_d is proved by the diols *(78)* and *(79)* which occur during the hydrolysis of beech lignin. The 12 sinapyl units may, therefore, occur in a random distribution spread between the units of scheme *(75)* as one mole syringaresinol *(77)* (minus 1 or 2 H-atoms), and also as dehydrogenated diols *(78)* and *(79)* (1 mole); or preferentialy *(80)* (5 moles), like unit 16 of the scheme *(75)*. If, furthermore, one β, γ-diaryl ether and two ketones are accepted, a scheme for beech lignin would result which corresponds with the composition given above. A combination with saccharides is likewise feasible. That dehydrogenated sinapyl alcohol forms no lignin-like substances is due to the preponderance of its radical type R_b *(25)* which, in absence of other radicals, forms only syringaresinol. It is not necessary to depict here this tentatively described constitutional model for beech lignin, but it may serve as a hypothesis which can be examined experimentally.

B. HOLMBERG (1934) has scanned the vast field of the plant kingdom by preparing the characteristic lignothioglycolic acids (p. 54). He boiled the plant material with hydrochloric acid in presence of thioglycolic acid. Under these conditions the result can be misleading if, along with lignin, or even in its absence, there are materials which are easily humified by the hydrochloric acid. From these two points of view one may observe the individual divisions of the plant kingdom as they are listed in A. Engler's "Syllabus of Plant Families" (1954 and 1964); then in division XII (*Fungi*), and XIII (*Lichens*) no lignin-type materials are to be found. Through Holmberg's results lignin in division XIV (*Bryophyta*) cannot be definitely demonstrated, and the lignin-type products from mosses described in the present work (Table 7), because of their high water-content, do not quite correspond to lignin, though otherwise many characteristics point to its presence, e. g. a low methoxyl content (LINDBERG and THEANDER, 1952; FR. and HARKIN, 1964; FR. 1964/65).

In division IV (*Pteridophyta*), *Lycopodium* and *Filices* (Ferns), lignins are to be met. In *Equisitales*, HOLMBERG has not found any lignin, which information is of interest when related to the origin of coal. In division XVI (*Gymnosperms*) the presence of lignin has been proved in all the plants examined. The coniferin-type lignin dominates; but there are two lignins from conifers (*Podocarpus* species) that appear to be more like hardwood lignin (CREIGHTON, GIBBS ana HIBBERT, 1944). In the last order, the *Gnetales* (e.g. *Ephedra*), the lignin approaches the composition of

Table 7. *Some recent analyses* (FR., 1964/5, 1965 b; FR. and HARKIN, 1964)

No. Various lignin preparations		Hydrogen atoms lost
1. Mixture of *p*-hydroxycinnamyl alcohols	$C_9H_{(10-i)}O_2[OCH_3]_i$	
2. DHP from *p*-coumaryl alcohol	$C_9H_{8.07}O_2[H_2O]_{0.40}$	1.93
3. Beech (*Fagus silvatica*)	$C_9H_{6.43}O_2[H_2O]_{0.53}[OCH_3]_{1.39}$	2.18
4. Mistletoe from Hackberry (*Viscum album* grown on *Celtis occidentalis*)	$C_9H_{6.75}O_2[H_2O]_{0.58}[OCH_3]_{1.41}$	1.74
5. Mistletoe from White Hawthorn (*Viscum album* grown on *Crataegus oxyacantha*)	$C_9H_{6.90}O_2[H_2O]_{0.60}[OCH_3]_{1.39}$	1.71
6. European (Norwegian etc.) Spruce (*Picea excelsa*)	$C_9H_{7.12}O_2[H_2O]_{0.40}[OCH_3]_{0.92}$	1.96
7. Mistletoe from Pine (Fir) (*Viscum album* grown on *Pinus silvestris*)	$C_9H_{7.02}O_2[H_2O]_{0.60}[OCH_3]_{0.94}$	2.09
8. Mistletoe from European silver fir (*Viscum album* grown on *Abies alba*)	$C_9H_{6.90}O_2[H_2O]_{0.56}[OCH_3]_{0.92}$	2.18
9. Lignin from Lignite (of *Taxodoxylon*, Bald Cypress), ca. 50 million years old	$C_9H_{7.29}O_2[H_2O]_{0.34}[OCH_3]_{0.69}$	2.02
10. Alfalfa (*Medicago sativum*)	$C_9H_{7.22}O_2[H_2O]_{0.41}[OCH_3]_{0.84}$	1.90
11. Lycopod (*Lycopodium obscurum*)	$C_9H_{7.37}O_2[H_2O]_{0.49}[OCH_3]_{0.73}$	1.90
12. Stalks of the moss *Polytrichum commune*	$C_9H_{7.94}O_2[H_2O]_{0.78}[OCH_3]_{0.25}$	1.81
13. Peat Moss (*Sphagnum*)	$C_9H_{7.96}O_2[H_2O]_{0.90}[OCH_3]_{0.25}$	1.79
	average	1.94

Explanation of Table 7

1. This depicts the general formula of the mixture of *p*-hydroxycinnamyl alcohols which are the basis of a lignin containing *i* methoxyl groups per C_9 unit.
2. The dehydrogenation product of *p*-coumaryl alcohol (FR. and GEHRKE, 1951, repeated by FR., HARKIN 1964) has the composition expected for a methoxyl-free lignin.
3. All lignin preparations 3 to 13 have been isolated as MW-lignin. In order to remove carbohydrates, it was treated with 70% sulfuric acid, following KLASON (1908). Nos 3 to 5 represent the hardwood type of lignin, nos 6 to 9 the coniferous (soft) wood type, and nos 10 to 13 lignin of different plants. The last column indicates the difference in hydrogen between lignin preparations and the corresponding mixture of *p*-hydroxycinnamic alcohols. The conversion of the alcohols into lignin is, within the limits of experimental error, associated with a loss of two atoms of hydrogen or a little less, the average of spruce lignin being 1.93 atoms (p. 69); 9.08—7.15 = 1.93.

4, 5, 7, 8. The four samples of mistletoe lignin are discussed on p. 114.

6. This lignin is taken from a 20-year-old spruce stem. Lignin of 1- or 2-year-old twigs, taken from 3- to 5-year-old spruce trees, has a methoxyl content like the lignins 9 and 11 (FR. and LEHMANN, 1963; FR., TORRES-SERRES, 1967 p. 98; cf. MANSKAJA, 1958).
9. See p. 115.
10. Alfalfa lignin seems to resemble the lignin of *Gramineae.*
11. The general composition of lycopod lignin resembles one year old conifer lignin. It contains little or none of the sinapyl component. The stalks which were used contained 37% of lignin (Klason method).
12. The stalks of *Polytrichum* gave 38% Klason lignin. The large amount of water figuring in the formulae of 12 and 13 is remarkable and differs from that of all other lignins.
13. The *Sphagnum* species from the Black Forest gave 4.4% of Klason lignin. After treatment with 70% sulfuric acid, the MW-lignin contained 4.5% OCH_3. This exceeds Lindberg's and Theander's finding (1952).

lignin of class XVII, namely that of *Angiosperms* and in particular that of *Dicotyledons*. Among these only the results on a few herbaceous plants, e.g. *Lathraea*, are uncertain. Among the *Monocotyledons*, from which two palms undoubtedly yielded lignin, the lignin-content of only two water-plants, *Potamogeton natans* and *Zostera marina*, is questionable. For further information see MANSKAJA, 1958.

These observations are taken to mean that in primitive plants the *p*-coumaryl alcohol component predominates over the small amount of coniferyl alcohol in the production of its lignin. In conifers the coniferyl alcohol predominates in higher orders of plants; the proportion of sinapyl alcohol in the mixture increases relatively.

The lignin of *Viscum album*, the central European mistletoe, deserves interest (FR., 1965, 1965 b). The plant is actually a dicotyledon which occurs in three varieties that are morphologically indistinguishable. One sort grows on numerous deciduous trees and can be transplanted within this group, e.g. from poplar onto apple trees or vice versa. The second variety grows on pines and cannot be transferred to hardwoods or other conifers. The third variety grows on silver fir (*Abies alba*) and can sometimes be grown with difficulty upon spruce and larch, but not on pine. It has been found that the mistletoe from deciduous trees contains a hardwood lignin (Table 7, Nos 4 and 5) while that from the two conifers (7, 8) contains a softwood lignin. It seems that the mistletoe withdraws the nutrients for its lignin synthesis from the host plant. In accordance with this postulate, mistletoe does not give an indigo staining with indican and therefore does not contain a detectable β-glucosidase. Consequently lignification in mistletoe is not preceded as in other plants by a glycosidic cleavage of glucosides of the three *p*-hydroxycinnamyl alcohols. Mistletoe seems to receive the preformed *p*-hydroxycinnamyl alcohols directly from the host tree. It is not known if the host tree delivers the alcohols to the mistletoe before glucosidation or after releasing them from their glucosides.

2. The Concept of Lignin

The lignins listed in Table 7 are so diverse that the question arises just how far the concept of lignin can be extended. The general limitation is given by the definition that lignin is an aromatic substance that differs from the carbohydrates and which fortifies the polysaccharides in plants, converting the tissues into wood. However, this precondition is not sufficient to define a lignin. It is conceivable that this same function could be fulfilled to some extent by silicilic acid, by tannins, other phenols, and their polymeric condensation products. They may in fact assist the lignin in this rôle in the heartwood of many trees. But they may not be grafted on the saccharides.

In order to indicate the boundaries of the definition of lignin, one must revert to the origin of the concept of lignin, principally spruce lignin. Spruce lignin is a product of the dehydrogenation of a mixture of the three *p*-hydroxycinnamyl alcohols. Hardwood lignins are also readily accommodated by this definition; it is merely the relative proportions of the three phenolic alcohols that differ. The principal characteristic of these lignins is their methoxyl content. However, when the methoxyl content becomes less and less towards sphagnum lignin, the question arises whether the material we call sphagnum lignin is really a lignin or not.

We must therefore apply additional criteria. Lignins give rise to Hibbert's ketones, to *p*-hydroxybenzaldehyde, vanillin, and frequently to syringaldehyde. The recalculation of the elemental composition of the lignin to a C_9-basis gives further evidence. When the oxygen in excess of two atoms is subtracted with the equivalent of hydrogen in the form of water, the formula becomes $C_9H_gO_2[H_2O]_h[OCH_3]_i$. When the polymer examined is a genuine lignin, *g* must be approximately equal to $10 - i - 2$ and *h* must not exceed the value 1.0, while *i* must lie between 0 and 1.5. In addition, a substance that can be regarded as being equivalent to the prototype of a lignin, namely spruce lignin, should be isolable, using the method for the production of spruce milled-wood lignin. The lignin in the plant should also be in chemical combination with the carbohydrates. Another characteristic feature of lignin is its ability to react with thioglycolic acid (p. 54, 68). Experience shows that no more than one molecule of thioglycolic acid can enter the lignin per C_9 unit. The formula for the basic lignin recalculated from the composition of the lignothioglycolic acid must fulfill the above conditions for the C_9 lignin formula. Nevertheless, it is obvious that the allocation of insoluble plant products of low methoxyl content to the class of lignins demands the exercise of considerable caution.

3. Fossilized Wood (Lignite)

A sample of conifer lignite (Taxodoxylon), about 50 million years old, was investigated (Table 7, No. 9). After removal of bitumen and similar substances, the lignite contained 6.8% of methoxyl. From this a MW-lignin was obtained in a yield of 20%. This was treated with 70% sulfuric acid to afford a lignin with 12.14% OCH_3 which had the composition shown in Table 7. After oxidation with nitrobenzene and alkali, the extracted lignite (6.8% OCH_3) yielded a small amount of syringaldehyde. The general impression is that it is a moderately oxidized coniferous lignin, in which the *p*-hydroxycoumaryl and guaiacyl nuclei had undergone a further condensation or it is a normal lignin resembling that of young spruce twigs (Fr., Heinichen and Harkin, 1966).

4. Humic Substances

During the formation of wood, the cells die when lignin formation is finished; the enzymes can no longer be observed. On the other hand, when fungi or other laccase- or peroxidase-containing organisms penetrate into the woody tissue, the lignin is attacked. Similarly, freshly prepared artificial lignin or MW-lignin, when kept continually moistened with water in the presence of toluene (to protect it against infection), can be attacked by laccase with air or peroxidase with hydrogen-peroxide. This means that the enzymes which build up lignin are able to degrade it slowly.

Much work has been done on the rotting of lignin-containing material by fungi and other organisms. In these experiments laccase or peroxidase act in the presence of the living organism. For the purpose of obtaining lignin degradation products, such experiments are not very instructive.

Humic acids may be formed from very different starting materials (SUNDMAN, 1965). Among these are the different kinds of lignin. A theory has been proposed that lignin is degraded to monomolecular quinones which recombine by polycondensation to humic substances. The schematic constitution of spruce lignin (*75*) shows that a general degradation to simple quinones is not possible (FR., 1962). Only a few units may be degraded to quinones. The main part of the structure should be rather resistant to degradation and would be expected to maintain a large size. Besides, it is not very probable that quinones under the conditions existing in the soil would recombine with each other to form larger aggregates. When simple quinones are formed, they find many other substances to react with, in addition to their own species.

K. Concluding Remark

There is no doubt that neither spruce lignin nor any other kind of lignin will ever be satisfactorily depicted by a single formula, even by a very extended one.

Presupposing, as we do, that the main kind of building stones and the mode of their interlinking are elucidated, we have to ask in the future for the frequency of their mutual occurrence; we have to ask for rare or overlooked bonds and units; and we have to establish the chemistry of hardwood lignin and lignin of other provenance.

The initial question, whether lignin has an understandable architecture, is answered: its constitution is clearly understood; but the classical concept of chemical architecture and methods must be extended and modified regarding this peculiar natural product.

L. References

Page numbers refer to text

ADLER, E.: Acta Chem. Scand. **2**, 93 (1948), p. 60, 72, 74.

— Paperija Puu **43**, 634 (1961), p. 74.

— Advances in Chem. Ser. **59**, IX (1966), p. 50, 52.

—, B. BECKER, T. ISHIHARA und A. STANWIK: Holzforschung **20**, 3 (1966); here, earlier literature dealing with hydroxyl and carbonyl distribution in lignin is quoted, p. 60, 72, 73.

—, and L. ELLMER: Acta Chem. Scand. **2**, 839 (1948), p. 60, 72, 74.

—, and J. GIERER: In: Treiber; Chemie der Pflanzenzellwand, p. 446. Berlin-Göttingen-Heidelberg: Springer 1957, p. 60, 74, 107.

—, and B. GUSTAFSON: Acta Chem. Scand. **17**, 27 (1963), p. 95.

—, and S. HERNESTAM: Acta Chem. Scand. **9**, 319 (1955), p. 71.

ALLEN, C. F. H., and J. R. BEYERS: J. Am. Chem. Soc. **71**, 2683 (1949), p. 83.

ANDERZÉN, O., u. B. HOLMBERG: Ber. **56**, 2544 (1923), p. 62, 81.

AULIN-ERDTMAN, G.: cf. Brauns and Brauns (1960) 2447, p. 71.

—, and Y. TOMITA: Acta Chem. Scand. **17**, 535 (1963), p. 86.

BAYLEY, A. J.: Eng. Chem. Anal. Ed. **8**, 52, 389 (1936), p. 93.

BEIJERINCK, M. W.: Koninkl. Ned. Akad. Wetenschap. Proc. **2**, 495 (1900), p. 99.

BENEDIKT, R., u. M. BAMBERGER: Monatsh. Chem. **11**, 260 (1890), p. 50.

BEYER, O.: Schweiz. Chemiker-Ztg., Beilage zu Technik und Industrie **1922**, 572, p. 48.

— Chem. Zentr. **1923** II, 155, p. 48.

Björkman, A.: Nature **174**, 1057 (1954), p. 52, 64.
— Svensk Papperstidn. **59**, 477 (1956), p. 52, 64.
— Svensk Papperstidn **60**, 158, 243, 285, 392 (1957), p. 52, 64.
Braconnot, H.: Ann. chim. phys. **12**, 172 (1819), p. 64.
Brauns, F. E.: J. Am. Chem. Soc. **61**, 2120 (1939), p. 52.
— The chemistry of lignin. New York: Acad. Press 1952, p. 51, 53, 64.
— In: Wise, L. E., and E. C. Jahn: Wood chemistry, 2. ed., Vol I, p. 517. New York: Reinhold publ. Co 1952 a, p. 74.
—, and D. A. Brauns: The chemistry of lignin, Supplement Volume. New York: Acad. Press 1960, p. 51, 53.
Brewer, C. P., L. M. Cooke, and H. Hibbert: J. Am. Chem. Soc. **70,** 57 (1948), p. 77.
Brockmann, H., u. G. Meyer: Ber. **86**, 1514 (1953), p. 71, 85.
Brown, W., S. J. Falkehag, and E. B. Cowling: Nature **214**, 410 (1967), p. 52.
Cousin, H., et H. Hérissey: Compt. rend. **146**, 1413 (1908), p. 75, 83.
— — Compt. rend. **147**, 247 (1909), p. 75, 83.
Cramer, A. B., J. M. Hunter, and H. Hibbert: J. Am. Chem. Soc. **61**, 509 (1939), p. 63, 76, 78.
Creighton, R. H. J., R. D. Gibbs, and H. Hibbert: J. Am. Chem. Soc. **66**, 37 (1944), p. 112.
Duerksen, J. D., and H. Halvorson: J. Biol. Chem. **233**, 1113 (1958), p. 99.
Engel, O., u. E. Wedekind: German Patent 581806 (1932), p. 51.
Englers Syllabus der Pflanzenfamilien **12.** Ed., Vol. I 1954, II 1964; Berlin-Nikolassee, Gebr. Bornträger; International Code of Botanical Nomenclature, Utrecht (1952). p. 112.
Enkvist, T., and T. Lindfors: Finska Kemist samfundets Medd. **75**, 1 (1966), p. 54.
Erdtman, H.: Liebigs Ann. Chem. **503**, 283 (1933), p. 60, 75.
— Biochem. Z. **258**, 172 (1933 a), p. 60, 75.
— Liebigs Ann. Chem. **516**, 162 (1935), p. 75.
— Svensk Kem. Tidskr. **48**, 236 (1936), p. 87.
— Svensk Papperstidn. **42**, 344 (1939), p. 75.
— Svensk Papperstidn. **43**, 255 (1940), p. 76, 106.
— Cellulosechemie **18**, 83 (1940 a), p. 76, 106.
— and J. Gripenberg: Acta Chem. Scand. 171 (1937), p. 81.
Fischer, Franz., H. Schrader, and A. Friedrich: Gesammelte Abhandl. zur Kenntnis d. Kohle **6**, 1, 1922/3, p. 81.
Fogelberg, B. C., K. Forss, and S. Fugleberg: Paperi ja Puu **49**, 725 (1967), p. 109.
Forss, K., and K. E. Fremer: Tappi **47**, 485 (1964), p. 109.
— — Paperi ja Puu **47**, 443 (1965), p. 109.
— —, and B. Stenlund: Paperi ja Puu **48**, 565, 669 (1966), p. 109.
Fredenhagen, K., u. G. Cadenbach: Angew. Chem. **46**, 113 (1933), p. 51.
Freudenberg, K.: Die Chemie der natürlichen Gerbstoffe. Berlin: Springer 1920, p. 48.
— Ber. **54**, 767 (1921), p.48, 49.
— Liebigs Ann. Chem. **433**, 230 (1923), p. 71.
— Liebigs Ann. Chem. **461**, 130 (1928). p. 49.
— Sitzungsber. Heidelberger Akad. d. Wissensch. 1928a, 19. Abh., p. 68, 75, 76.
— Tannin, Cellulose Lignin. Berlin: Springer 1933, p. 49.
— Stereochemistry, p. 662. Wien: Deuticke 1933 a, p. 50, 95, 97.
— Fortschr. Chem. org. Naturstoffe **2**, 1 (1939), p. 59, 76.
— Angew. Chem. **52**, 362 (1939 a), p. 61, 76.
— Ann. Rev. Biochem. **8**, 81 (1939 b), p. 76.
— Svensk Kem. Tidskr. **55**, 201 (1943), p. 61.
— Papier, Das **1**, 209 (1947), p. 59.
— Angew. Chem. **60**, 125 (1948), p. 59.
— Sitzungsber. Heidelberger Akad. d. Wissensch. **5**, 151 (1949), p. 61.
— Fortschr. Chem. org. Naturstoffe **11**, 43 (1954), p. 61.
— Festschrift L. Ruzicka, Croat. Chem. Acta **29**, 189 (1957), p. 83.
— In: Fourth internat. Congr. of Biochemistry (Wien 1958), Vol. II, Biochemistry of wood, p. 121. London: Pergamon Press 1959, p. 61.
— Holz als Roh- u. Werkstoff **18**, 282 (1960), p. 111.

FREUDENBERG, K.: Fortschr. Chem. org. Naturstoffe **20**, 1 (1962), p. 47, 65, 86, 105, 111, 116.
— Pure and Appl. Chem. **5**, 9 (1962 a), p. 47.
— Stärke **15**, 199 (1963), p. 49.
— Brennstoff-Chem. **44**, 328 (1963 a), p. 52, 85.
— Holzforschung **18**, 3 (1964), p. 72, 84.
— In: The formation of wood in forest trees. New York: Academic Press 1964 a, p. 47.
— In: Chimie et biochimie de la lignine, de la cellulose et des hémicelluloses, p. 39. Imprimeries Réunies de Chambéry 1964/1965, p. 72, 112, 113.
— Science **148**, 595 (1965), p. 47, 49, 105, 114.
— Coochbehar lectures. Indian Assoc. Cultivation Sci. 1965 a (delivered March 1958), p. 49, 50.
— In: Festschrift KURT MOTHES, p. 167. Jena 1965 b, p. 100, 113, 114.
— Advances in Chem. Ser. **59**, 1 (1966); cf. 1964; FR. and HARKIN, 1964; FR., 1964/65; FR., 1965 b, p. 47, 78, 80, 86.
— E. Fischer's contribution to carbohydrate chemistry. Advances in Carbohydrate Chem. **21**, 1 (1966 a), p. 48, 50.
— Ber. **100**, CLXXII (1967), p. 48, 49.
— Holzforschung **22**, 65 (1968) p. 110.
—, u. K. ADAM: Ber. **74**, 387 (1941), p. 63.
—, W. BELZ u. CHR. NIEMANN: Ber. **62**, 1554 (1929), p. 58.
—, u. F. BITTNER: Ber. **83**, 600 (1950), p. 83, 111.
— — Ber. **86**, 155 (1953), p. 61, 99.
—, O. BÖHME und L. PURRMANN: Ber. **55**, 1734 (1922), p. 48.
—, u. E. BRAUN: Communicated in FR., F. SOHNS, W. DÜRR und CHR. NIEMANN, Cellulosechemie **12**, 263 (1931), p. 59. 83, 106.
—, u. C. L. CHEN: Ber. **93**, 2533 (1960), p. 78.
— — Ber. **100**, 3683 (1967), p. 78, 80, 88.
— — u. G. CARDINALE: Ber. **95**, 2814 (1962), p. 78, 80, 81.
— —, J. M. HARKIN, H. NIMZ, and H. RENNER: Chem. Commun. **1965**, 224, p. 65, 75, 78, 86, 87, 89, 96, 100, 111.
—, u. K. DALL: Naturwissenschaften **42**, 606 (1955), p. 71.
—, u. G. DIETRICH: Liebigs Ann. Chem. **563**, 146 (1949), p. 61, 65.
—, u. H. DIETRICH: Ber. **86**, 4, (1953), p. 81.
—, u. W. DÜRR: Ber. **63**, 2713 (1930), p. 59.
— — Handbuch der Pflanzenanalyse, III. Wien: Springer 1932, p. 75.
—, u. W. EISENHUT: Ber. **88**, 626 (1955), p. 88.
—, K. ENGLER, E. FLICKINGER, A. SOBEK und F. KLINK: Ber. **71**, 1810 (1938), p. 60, 62, 76.
—, u. M. FRIEDMANN: Ber. **93**, 2138 (1960), p. 91.
—, u. W. FUCHS: Ber. **87**, 1924 (1954), p. 51, 55.
—, u. H. GEIGER: Ber. **96**, 1265 (1963), p. 88.
—, u. G. GEHRKE, Ber. **84**, 443 (1951), p. 113.
—, u. G. GRION: Ber. **92**, 1355 (1959), p. 93.
— — u. J. M. HARKIN: Angew. Chem. **70**, 743 (1958), p. 83, 87.
—, u. U. HARDER: Ber. **60**, 581 (1927), p. 57, 60.
— — u. L. MARKERT: Ber. **61**, 1760 (1928), 51, 58, 60.
—, u. J. M. HARKIN: Ber. **93**, 2814 (1960), p. 93.
— — Phytochemistry **2**, 189 (1963), 86, 87, 88, 89, 91, 98, 100.
— — Holzforschung **18**, 166 (1964), p. 72, 104, 110, 112, 113.
— —, M. REICHERT u. T. FUKUZUMI: Ber. **91**, 581 (1958), p. 111.
— — u. H. K. WERNER: Ber. **97**, 909 (1964), p. 53, 54, 71, 73, 92, 94.
—, G. HEINICHEN, and J. M. HARKIN: Not published p. 115.
—, u. H. HESS: Liebigs Ann. Chem. **448**, 121 (1926), p. 57, 75.
—, u. H. H. HÜBNER: Ber. **85**, 1181 (1952), p. 50, 83, 85, 86, 111.
—, u. O. IVERS: Ber. **55**, 929 (1922), p. 48.
—, A. JANSON, E. KNOPF u. A. HAAG: Ber. **69**, 1415 (1936), p. 76, 78.
—, K. JONES u. H. RENNER: Ber. **96**, 1844 (1963), p. 100.
—, u. V. JOVANOVIĆ: Ber. **96**, 2178 (1963), p. 102, 108, 111.

— — u. F. Topfmeier: Ber. **94**, 3227 (1961), p. 102, 108, 111.
—, F. Klink, E. Flickinger u. A. Sobek: Ber. **72**, 217 (1939), p. 60, 61, 76.
—, u. L. Knof: Ber. **90**, 2857 (1957), p. 52, 89, 100.
—, u. R. Kraft: Ber. **83**, 536 (1950). p. 54.
— — u. W. Heimberger: Ber. **84**, 472 (1951), p. 99, 111.
—, L. Lautenschläger u. H. Tausend: Liebigs Ann. Chem. **685**, 139 (1965), p. 63.
—, u. W. Lautsch: Naturwissenschaften **27**, 227 (1939), p. 61.
— — u. J. Brenck: German Pat. 947365 (1939), issued 1956, p. 61.
— — u. K. Engler: Ber. **73**, 167 (1940), p. 61.
— — u. G. Piazolo: Ber. **74**, 1879 (1941), p. 62.
— — — Cellulosechemie **21**, 95 (1943), p. 59.
— — — Cellulosechemie **22**, 97 (1944), p. 53.
— — — u. A. Scheffer: Ber. **74**, 171 (1941), p. 63.
—, u. B. Lehmann: Ber. **93**, 1354 (1960), p. 53, 85—88.
— — Ber. **96**, 1850 (1963), p. 53, 70, 98, 100, 101, 113.
—, M. Meister u. E. Flickinger: Ber.**70**, 500 (1937), p. 76.
—, u. H. F. Müller: Ber. **71**, 1821 (1938), p. 60.
— — Ber. **71**, 2500 (1938 a), p. 59.
—, u. H. Nimz: Ber. **95**, 2057 (1962), p. 91.
— — Chem. Comm. **1966**, 132, p. 89, 96, 97.
—, u. K. Penzien: Ber. **102**, (1969), p. 101.
—, u. E. Plankenhorn: Ber. **75**, 857 (1942), p. 51.
— — Ber. **80**, 149 (1947), p. 61.
—, u. Th. Ploetz: Ber. **73**, 754 (1940), p. 64.
—, u. D. Rasenack: Ber. **86**, 755 (1953), p. 84.
—, u. K.-Chr. Renner: Ber. **98**, 1879 (1965), p. 88.
—, H. Reznik, H. Boesenberg u. D. Rasenack: Ber. **85**, 641 (1952), p. 98, 99, 99 footn.
— —, Werner Fuchs u. M. Reichert: Angew. Chem. **66**, 109 (1954), p. 98, 99.
— — — — Naturwissenschaften **42**, 29 (1955), p. 98, 99.
—, u. H. Richtzenhain: Ber. **76**, 997 (1943), p. 82.
—, and A. Sakakibara: Liebigs Ann. Chem. **623**, 129 (1959), p. 92.
—, u. H. Schlüter: Ber. **88**, 617 (1955), p. 66, 71, 87, 88.
—, K. Seib u. K. Dall: Ber. **92**, 807 (1959), p. 54, 70, 71.
—, and G. S. Sidhu: Tetrahedron Letters **20**, 3 (1960), p. 87.
— — Ber. **94**, 831 (1961), p. 87.
— — Holzforschung **15**, 33 (1961 a), p. 110.
—, u. F. Sohns: Ber. **66**, 262 (1933), p. 61.
— —, W. Dürr u. Chr. Niemann: Cellulosechemie **12**, 263 (1931), p. 59, 83.
— — u. A. Janson: Liebigs Ann. Chem. **518**, 83 (1935), p. 59, 71.
—, u. M. Swaleh: Ber. **102**, (1969), p. 83, 101, 106.
—, u. H. Tausend: Ber. **96**, 2081 (1963), p. 91.
— — Ber. **97**, 3418 (1964), p. 92.
—, F. P. Toribio, K. Penzien u. O. P. Garg: Ber. **102**, (1969), p. 101.
—, u. J. Torres-Serres: Liebigs Ann. Chem. **654**, 160 (1962), p. 63.
— — Liebigs Ann. Chem. **703**, 225 (1967), p. 98, 100, 113.
—, u. H. Walch: Ber. **76**, 305 (1943), p. 57.
—, u. E. Weber: Angew. Chem. **38**, 280 (1925), p. 71.
—, u. K. Weinges: Angew. Chem. **74**, 182 (1962), p. 50.
— — Angew. Chem. Internat. Edit. **1**, 158 (1962 a), p. 50.
— — Bull. Nat. Inst. Sci. India **24**, 31 (1965) (Receiv. August 1964), p. 50.
—, u. H. K. Werner: Ber. **97**, 579 (1964), p. 94.
—, H. Zocher u. W. Dürr: Ber. **62**, 1814 (1929), p. 51, 60, 75.
Fuchs, Walter: Ber. **54**, 484 (1921), p. 56.

Gierer, J.: Acta Chem. Scand. **8**, 1319 (1954), p. 72.
Goldschmidt, O.: Cf. Brauns, F. E., and D. A. Brauns (1960, p. 213); p. 71.
Grafe, V.: Monatsh. Chem. **25**, 987 (1904), p. 55, 61.
Gripenberg, J.: Acta Chem. Scand. **2**, 82 (1948), p. 87.

HÄGGLUND, E.: Ark. f. Kemi **7**, 1 (1818), p. 69.
— Svensk Kem. Tidskr. **37**, 116 (1925), p. 53, 76.
— Svensk Kem. Tidskr. **38**, 177 (1926), p. 53, 76.
—, and C. J. MALM: Acta Acad. Aboensis, Math. et Phys. **2**, No. 4 (1922), p. .69
HARKIN, J. M.: Fortschr. chem. Forsch. **6**, 101 (1966), p. 47, 52.
— Oxidative Coupling of Phenols, p. 1, New York 1967.
— Unpublished work, 1966/67, p. 52, 54, 64, 84.
HARRIS, E. E., J. D'IANNI, and H. ADKINS: J. Am. Chem. Soc. **60**, 1467 (1938), p. 63.
HARTLER, N., P. RÖNSTRÖM, and L. STOCKMAN: Svensk Papperstidn. **64**, 194 (1961), p. 53.
HERNESTAM, S.: Svensk Kem. Tidskr. **67**, 37 (1955), p. 71.
HERZOG, R. O., u. A. HILLMER: Ber. **60**, 365 (1927), p. 60.
— — Z. physiol. Chem. Hoppe-Seyler's **168**, 117 (1927 a), p. 60.
—, u. W. JANCKE: Z. Physik **III**, 196 (1920), p. 60.
HIGUCHI, T.: Biochemistry (Japan) **45**, 515 (1958), p. 83.
HILPERT, R. S.: Ber. **69**, 1509 (1936), p. 56.
—, u. H. HELLWAGE: Ber. **68**, 380 (1935), p. 59.
—, E. LITTMANN u. R. WIENBECK: Ber. **70**, 560 (1937), p. 56.
HOLMBERG, B.: Ing. Vetenskaps Akad. Handl. No. **103** (1930), p. 54, 60, 64.
— Ing. Vetenskaps Akad. Hand.l No. **131** (1934), p. 60, 112.
— Papir-J. **23**, 88, 92 (1935), p. 60, 76.
— Svensk Papperstidn. **39**, special No. **113** (1936), p. 60, 63, 76.
— Ber. **75**, 1760 (1942), p. 60, 65, 76.
—, and K. GRALÉN: Ing. Vetenskaps Akad. Handl. **1942**, No. 162, p. 65, 76.
IUPAC Rules A 13,3: J. Am. Chem. Soc. **82**, 5552 (1960), p. 55.
JENSEN, W., B. C. FOGELBERG, K. FORSS, K. E. FREMER u. M. JOHANSON: Holzforschung **20**, 48 (1966); for further quotations see here, p. 109.
KARRER, P., u. F. WIDMER: Helv. Chim. Acta **4**, 174 (1921), p. 49.
KLASON, P.: Tek. Tidskr. Afdeling Kemi, Metallurgi **23**, 49 (1893), p. 63.
— Svensk Kem. Tidskr. **9**, 133 (1897), p. 55.
— Arkiv Kemi **2**, 36 (1907), p. 55.
— Bericht über die Hauptversammlung des Vereins der Zellstoff- und Papierchemiker **1908**, 52; cf. ftn. 57, 58, p. 50, 53, 55, 64, 69, 113.
— Arkiv Mineral. Geol. **4**, No. 6 (1911) p. 50, 55. A complete bibliography of Klason's disseminated papers: B. HOLMBERG, Kungl. svenska Vetenskapsakademiens Årsbok för 1953. (Yearbook 1953, Swedish Royal Academy of Science).
— Beiträge zur Kenntnis der chemischen Zusammensetzung des Fichtenholzes, Schriften des Vereins der Zellstoff- und Papierchemiker. Berlin, edit. BORNTRÄGER, 1911 a, p. 50, 55.
— Ber. **58**, 375, 1761 (1925), p. 55.
KOHLER, E. P., and M. REIMER: Am. Chem. Soc. J. **31**, 178 (1904), p. 57.
KRATZL, K.: Monatsh. Chem. **78**, 173 (1948), p. 61.
—, G. BILLEK, E. KLEIN u. L. BUCHTELA: Monatsh. Chem. **88**, 721 (1957), p. 99.
KUHN, R., u. F. D'ORSA: Angew. Chem. 847 (1931), p. 61.
—, u. H. ROTH: Ber. **66**, 1274 (1933), p. 61.
KÜRSCHNER, K.: Zur Chemie der Ligninkörper, p. 94. Stuttgart: Enke 1925, p. 57.
KÜSTER, W., u. R. DAUER: Cellulosechemie **11**, 4 (1930), p. 59.
LANGE, P. W.: Svensk Papperstidn. **47**, 262 (1944), p. 60.
— Svensk Papperstidn. **48**, 241 (1945), p. 60.
LEOPOLD, B.: Svensk Kem. Tidskr. **64**, 1 (1952), p. 62, 81.
— Acta Chem. Scand. **6**, 38 (1952 a), p. 62, 81.
— Svensk Papperstidn. **55**, 816 (1952 b), p. 62, 81.
—, and J. L. MALMSTRÖM: Acta Chem. Scand. **5**, 936 (1951), p. 61.
LINDBERG, B., and O. THEANDER: Acta Chem. Scand. **6**, 311 (1952), p. 112, 113.
LINDGREN, B. O.: Svensk Papperstidn. **55**, 78 (1952), p. 76, 106.
LUDWIG, C. H., B. J. NIST, and J. L. MCCARTHY: J. Am. Chem. Soc. **86**, 1186 (1964), p. 86, 108, 109.
MADSEN, J.: Dissertation, Hannover Techn. Hochschule **1917**, p. 48.
MANSKAJA, S. M.: Congr. Biochem. Wien (1858) II, 215, Pergam. Pr. 1959, p. 98, 113, 114.

MANSKAJA, S. M.: Proceedings of the IV. International Congress of Biochemistry, Vol. 2: Biochemistry of Wood, Wien 1958, p. 224. London: Pergamon Press 1959.
MARTON, J., and E. ADLER: Tappi **46**, 92 (1963), p. 63, 74.
MELAMID, M.: Private communication to the author, Nov. 30th, 1923, p. 48.
— Engl. Pat. 194723 (12. 3. 1922) Chem. Zentr. **1926**, I, 3642, p. 48.
NEISH, A. C.: Preceding article (1968), p. 47.
NIKITIN, W. M., and M. KROSHILOVA: Bumazh. Prom. Nos. 2, 3, 4 (1965), p. 59.
NIMZ, H.: Ber. **96**, 478 (1963), p. 52, 83.
— Angew. Chem. **76**, 597 (1964), p. 88.
— Ber. **98**, 533 (1965), p. 88, 96.
— Ber. **98**, 3153 (1965 a), p. 111.
— Ber. **98**, 3160 (1965 b), p. 111.
— Holzforschung **20**, 105 (1966), p. 96, 111.
— Ber. **99**, 469 (1966 a), p. 75, 95, 96, 111.
— Ber. **99**, 2638 (1966 b), p. 96, 111.
— Ber. **100**, 181 (1967) p. 96.
— Ber. **100**, 2633 (1967 a), p. 88, 97.
—, u. H. GABER: Ber. **98**, 538 (1965), p. 96, 111.
OGIYAMA, K., and T. KONDO: Mokuzai Gakkaishi **11**, 206 (1965), p. 81.
— — Tetrahedron Letters **1966**, 2083, p. 81.
OST, H.: Liebigs Ann. Chem. **398**, 338 (1913), p. 48.
PAYEN, A.: Compt. rend. **7**, 1057, 1125 (1838); cf. E. ADLER (1966), p. 50, 56, 72.
PEARL, J. A.: The Chemistry of Lignin, E. Arnold Ed., London 1967 and M. Dekker Inc., New York 1967, p. 87, 110.
PEW, J. C.: J. Am. Chem. Soc. **77**, 2831 (1955), p. 62.
— Nature **193**, 250 (1962), p. 102, 108.
— J. Org. Chem. **28**, 1048 (1963), p. 102, 108.
READ, D. E., and C. B. PURVES: J. Am. Chem. Soc. **74**, 116 (1952), p. 62, 80.
REINITZER, F.: Arch. Pharm. **252**, 341 (1914), p. 83.
RICHTZENHAIN, H.: Ber. **75**, 269 (1942), p. 62, 81.
— Ber. **77**, 409 (1944), p. 82.
— Ber. **81**, 260 (1948), p. 82.
— Ber. **82**, 405 (1949), p. 82.
— Ber. **83**, 488 (1950), p. 78.
— Svensk Papperstidn. **53**, 644 (1950 a), p. 78.
ROBERTSON, A.: J. Chem. Soc. **1927**, 1939 (1900), p. 99 footn.
SANDBERG, G.: "Abisko", Serien Sveriges Nationalparker, p. 18. Stockholm: Raben and Sjögren 1960, p. 99.
SANKEY, C. A., and H. HIBBERT: Can. J. Research. **5**, 1 (1931), p. 56.
SARKANEN, K. Y.: In: BROWNING, B. L., The chemistry of wood, p. 249. New York, London: Interscience 1963, p. 76, 106.
SARKAR, P. B.: J. Indian Chem. Soc. **11**, 691 (1934), p. 60.
SCHRAUTH, W.: Ang. Chem. **36**, 150 (1923), p. 56.
SCHUBERT, W., and F. F. NORD: J. Am. Chem. Soc. **72**, 977 (1950) and later papers, p. 52.
SCHULZE, L.: German Patent application 111993 (1940), p. 61.
SCHÜTZ, FR.: Angew. Chem. **56**, 179 (1943), p. 56, 59, 96.
—, P. SARTEN u. H. MEYER: Angew. Chem. **60**, 115 (1948), p. 56, 59, 96.
—, u. W. KNACKSTEDT: Cellulosechemie **20**, 15 (1942), p. 51.
SHORYGINA, N. N., and YA. T. KEFELI: Zhur. Obshcheĭ Khim. **18**, 528 (1948), p. 63.
SPÄTH, W., F. WESSELY u. L. KORNFELD: Ber. **65**, 1536 (1932), p. 89.
STINNES, H.: Riebeck Montan und Ölwerke, D.R. Pat. 423096 (12. 3. 1922), Chem. Zentrbl. 1926 I, 3642, p. 48.
STUMPF, W.: Svensk Papperstidn., Hägglund jubilee Vol. **1947**, 164, p. 63.
—, u. K. FREUDENBERG: Angew. Chem. **62**, 447, 537 (1950), p. 51.
—, F. WEYGAND u. O. GROSSKINSKI: Ber. **86**, 1391 (1953), p. 51.
—, u. E. WIESENBERGER: Cellulosechemie **18**, 103 (1940), p. 64.
SUNDMAN, V.: Acta Polytech. Chem. Mety. Ser. **40**, 116 (1965), p. 116.

TIEMANN, F., u. W. HAARMANN: Ber. **7**, 608 (1874), p. 83.
—, u. B. MENDELSOHN: Ber. **8**, 1136 (1875), p. 55.
UNGAR, E.: Beiträge zur Kenntnis der verholzten Faser, Thesis, Eidgen. Techn. Hochschule Zürich; printed in 1916 in Budapest, p. 49, 56.
URBAN, H.: Thesis, Techn. Hochschule Karlsruhe (1926), p. 51, 54, 57, 64, 69, 75.
— Cellulosechemie **7**, 73 (1926 a), p. 51, 54, 57, 64, 69, 75.
VERLEY, A., u. FR. BÖLSING: Ber. **34**, 3354 (1901), p. 70.
WEST, E., A. A. MACINNES, and H. HIBBERT: J. Am. Chem. Soc. **65**, 1187 (1943); and other publications by HIBBERT, p. 63, 76, 78.
WIECHERT, K.: Cellulosechemie **18**, 57 (1940), p. 51.
WIESENBERGER, E.: Mikrochemie **30**, 241 (1942), p. 61, 71.
— Mikrochemie **33**, 51 (1947), p. 61, 71.
WILLSTÄTTER, R., u. L. KALB: Ber. **55**, 2637 (1922), p. 56, 57.
—, u. L. ZECHMEISTER: Ber. **46**, 2405 (1913), p. 51, 64.
ZECHMEISTER, L.: Zur Kenntnis der Cellulose und des Lignins, Dissertation, Eidgen. Techn. Hochschule Zürich 1911, p. 56.
ZIEGLER, E., u. K. GARTLER: Monatsh. Chem. **79**, 637 (1948), p. 72.
— — Monatsh. Chem. **80**, 634 (1949), p. 72.
ZINCKE, TH., u. O. HAHN: Liebigs Ann. Chem. **329**, 1 (1903), p. 94.

Subject Index

Acer Negundo 18—26
Acetaldehyde 13, 22, 61
Acetaminocinnamic acid-β-^{14}C 26
Acetate 11, 27
Acetate, pathway 27
Acetate-1-^{14}C 24
Acetate-2-^{14}C 23
Acetone powder 14
Acetophenones 32
Acid lignin 26
S-Adenosylmethionine: catechol O-methyl-transferase 31
Aerobacter aerogenes 15
Alcohol, benzyl 76
—, glucocoumaryl 98, 100
—, primary 72—74
—, tertiary 74
Alfalfa 113
Algae 34
—, green 34
Aliphatic hydroxyl 71
Alisma triviale 18, 25
Alkali and nitrobenzene, oxidation 61
Alkaloids 32
—, phenylethyl amine 33
Amaryllida 33
Amaryllidaceae 31
Amino acids, aromatic 15—17, 28, 29
— —, biosynthesis of aromatic 15
— —, phenylpropanoid 8, 16, 28, 33
α-Amino acids 16
p-Aminobenzoic acid 15
Ammonia-lyases 28—30
Analogues, caffeyl 30
—, guaiacyl 30
—, *m*-methoxy 30
Analyses, elemental 69
—, expression of lignin 65
— for methyllignin 67
— for acetyl-lignin 66
Angiosperms 3, 12, 13, 27, 28, 114
Animal tissues 31
Animals 15
p-Anisic acid (carboxyl-labelled) 24
Anisole series, compounds of 80
Anthocyanins 33, 36
Anthocyanin biosynthesis 33
—, formation 33
Anthranilic acid 15
Apples 14, 31
Aroxyl radical 85
Artifact, aromatic 57
Aspen twigs 28
ATP 31
Auxotroph 15
Avena sativa 19

Bacteria 15—17
Barley shoots 14
Basidiomycetes 30
Benzenediazonium sulfonic acid 56
Benzenepentacarboxylic acid 89
Benzoic acid, carboxyl-labelled 24
—, glucosides of hydroxylated 32
Benzyl alkyl ethers 63
— aryl ethers 63, 93, 105
— — ether, polymeric 94
Bifunctional compounds 48
— molecular residues, linking 50
Biosynthesis of aromatic amino acids in plants 15
Biphenyl bonds 108
— — in lignin 102
Biphenyl carbon skeleton 62
Bromus arvensis 19
— *inermis* 18, 20
Buckwheat 11, 16
By-products, metabolic 36

Caffeic acid 28—31, 33
— acid-β-^{14}C 21
Calamagrostis inexpansa 18, 20, 25
Cambial scrapings 31
— sap 32, 100
Caragana arborescens 18, 25
Carbohydrates 15, 17, 27, 28, 34, 35, 37
—, ether-type linkages with lignin 93, 95
—, lignin grafted onto 93
$^{14}CO_2$ 11, 29
C_6-C_3-skeleton 77
C_9 basis 65
Carbon dioxide 12, 27—29
Carbonyl groups 72, 74
— —, total 74
Carboxyl group, activation 30

Carex atherodes 20
— *laeviconica* 18, 25
Catechin 48, 50
Catechol 31
—, compounds 78
Cauliflower buds 16
Cellobiose 48, 49
Cellulose 48, 50, 56
— formula 49
Chlorogenic acid 29, 33
Chromatography, column 85
Chorismic acid 15
Cinnamaldehyde group 74
Cinnamic acid 28—30, 33, 36
— —, acetone-insoluble ester 29
— — -β-^{14}C 21
— —, carboxyl-labelled 21
— — derivatives 8, 17, 28, 30, 31, 33, 34, 37
— —, ester 36
— —, exogenous 29
— —, glucosides of hydroxylated 32
— —, labelled 28
— — -ring, β-^{14}C 21
— —, ring-substituted 17, 28
— — -α-^{14}C 21
— alcohol, glucosides of hydroxylated 32
Cinnamoyl quinates 29, 33
Cinnamyl alcohol 31, 37
— — derivatives 8, 37
— —, substituted 34
Colchicine 34
Colorado spruce 11
Compounds, bifunctional 48
— of the anisole series 80
— of the catechol (veratrole series 78
—, polymeric natural 48
—, trimethoxybenzene series 80
Condensation, acid-catalysed 96
Coniferin 11, 28, 31, 32, 55
Coniferin-β-^{14}C 22
Coniferin-(carbinol-^{14}C) 22
— -(L-glucoside) 26
Coniferin-α-^{14}C 22
D-Coniferin from L-phenyalanine-^{14}CO**2H** in spruce 100
L-Coniferin 99
Coniferous woods 13
Coniferyl alcohol 3, 31, 32, 34 55, 70
— — addition to the dimeric quinone methide 91
— —, dehydrogenation 82, 85
— —, deuterated 102
Coniferyl aldehyde 3, 32
Cordyline 99
Cortaderio selloana 31

p-Coumaric acid 14, 15, 17, 28—30, 32
— — derivatives 37
— acid-β-^{14}C 21
— acid-α-^{14}C 21
Coumarins 14, 32, 33
p-Coumaryl alcohol 34, 55, 70
— quinate 29
Coupling 34
—, stereospecific 34

Dactylis glomerata 19
Daucus carota 19
Decarboxylation 33
Degradation, mechanical, of lignin 52
Dehydrogenation of coniferyl alcohol 82, 55
— of mixture of three *p*-hydroxycinnamyl alcohols 82
—, phenols 75
— product (DHP) 84
Dehydropolymerization 3, 8, 32, 34
5-Dehydroquinate hydro-lyase 16
Dehydroquinic acid 16
Dehydroshikimic acid 16, 17
Demethoxylation reaction 28
Demethylation 28
Diazonium compounds 59
Dicotyledons 114
Dihydrocinnamic acid-β-^{14}C 20
Dihydroconiferyl alcohol 13, 19, 21, 23, 24, 26, 27
Dihydrosinapyl alcohol 13, 19, 21, 24, 26
Dilignols 85, 86
Dilution value 13
Dimethyl sulfate 12, 54
Distribution, countercurrent 85
Donor, methyl 31

Eleagnus commutata 18, 25
Enzymes 14, 16, 17, 30, 31, 36, 37
—, plant 14
Equistales 112
Erythrose 4-phosphate 17
Esters 28, 30—32, 36, 37
—, acetone-insoluble 29
—, alcohol-soluble 28
—, cinnamic 34
—, cinnamoyl 33
—, — glucose 33
—, coenzyme A 30
—, ferulic acid 31, 32
—, insoluble 29, 31
Esters, phenolic acid 14
—, soluble 28, 29
Escherichia coli 15
Ethanol lignin 23
Ethanolysis 12, 13
— products 13

Ether, benzyl 76
—, — aryl in lignin 93, 94, 105
—, carbohydrate lignol 93
— linkages between carbohydrates and lignin 95
— — in lignin 57
— oxygen 72
Eucalyptus 33
Eucalyptus 28
— *camaldulensis* 19, 25, 30
— *bicostata* 30
— *nitens* 23
— *sideroxylon* 19, 20, 24, 29, 30
— *regnans* 30
Eugenol 32, 58
Evolution 34—37
— in the plant kingdom 34
— of lignification 36
Excretion 36, 37
Experiment, spreading 59
Extractive-free plant material 12
— residue 25

Fagopyrum tataricum 16, 18, 20, 25, 26
Fagus sylvatica 110
Ferns 3
Ferulic acid 17, 28, 29, 31, 32
— — esters 32
— acid-2-^{14}C 32
— acid-α-^{14}C 21
— acid-β-^{14}C 21
Filices 112
Flaminia festucacea 20
Flavonoids 32, 33
Flavonoid compounds 14
Formaldehyde 57
—, liberation of 60
Formic acid 12
Fungi 34
—, secondary metabolic products of 33

Gallotannins 48
Genetic control 33
Gingko biloba 19
p-Glucocoumaryl alcohol 98, 100
Glucose 11, 27, 28
—, ^{14}C-labelled 11
Glucose-1-^{14}C 27
D-Glucose-1-^{14}C 11
Glucose 6-phosphate 16
β-Glucosidase 98
—, temperature coefficient 99
Glucosides 32
Glucosides of sinapyl and *p*-coumaryl alcohol 32, 98, 100
Glutamic acid 17
Glycolic acid oxidase 16
Glycosides 34
Gnetales 112
Gramineae 29
Grasses 30, 32, 37
Guaiacyl derivatives 13, 27, 28
— nuclei of lignin 27, 28
Guaiacylglycerol, etherified 75
Guaiacylpropane 76
Gymnosperms 3, 28

Hemipinic acids 12, 19
Hibbert's ketones 12, 19, 21—24, 26, 27, 108
Higher plants 36
Histochemical radioautography 22, 24, 26
Homoveratrol (C-methyl labelled) 25
Hordeum vulgare 18—20
Humic substances 115
Hydrobenzoic acids 28, 32, 33
Hydrochloric acid, ploroglucinol in 98
Hydrogenolysis 13, 27
Hydrocoumarans 75, 76
Hydrolases 14
Hydroxy acids 16
α-Hydroxy acids 16
p-Hydroxybenzaldehyde 12
—, (carbonyl-labelled) 24
p-Hydroxybenzoic acid 15
— —, (carboxyl-labelled) 22
Hydroxycinnamic acid 29
p-Hydroxycinnamyl alcohol 32
5-Hydroxyferulic acid 31
— acid-α-^{14}C 23
Hydroxyl, aliphatic 71
— estimation 70
—, secondary 71, 74
Hydroxylase 30
Hydroxylation 16, 30, 31, 36
— reaction 30
Ortho-Hydroxylation 33
Hydroxy-matairesinol 100
p-Hydroxyphenyllactic acid 29
DL-*p*-Hydroxyphenyllactic acid 26
DL-*p*-Hydroxyphenyllactic acid-β-^{14}C 20
p-Hydroxyphenylpyruvate 29, 30
Hydroxyphenylpyruvate 33
p-Hydroxyphenylpyruvic acid 29
— —, (carboxyl-labelled) 20
— acid-β-^{14}C 20, 26

Identity of lignification *in vivo* and *vitro* 98
Implantation 10, 11
Incorporation 27—29
—, efficiency of 17
— of ^{14}C 13, 16, 27
Index, refractive 60

Indican 99
Indigo 99
Indophenol reaction 71
Infusion technique 10, 11, 29
Intermediate, lignification 85
—, natural 10, 29, 32
—, obligate 10, 15
Isatis tinctoria 99
Isoflavones 33
Isohemipinic acid 19, 27
— — from labelled DHP 101
— — — lignin grown with labelled coniferin 101
— — grown with labelled phenylalamine 101
Isomerization 33

Juncus bufonius 18, 25
— *nodosus* 18, 25
Jute cellulose 60

Klason lignin 20, 21, 64, 113

Laccase 83
Legumes 14, 30
Lepachys columniferae 18, 25
Lichens, secondary metabolic products of 33
Life, origin of 36
Lignans 34
Lignification 34
— *in vivo* and *in vitro* 98
— intermediates 85
Lignin 4, 12, 14, 27—32, 34, 36, 37
—, acetic acid 51
—, acetyl- 66
—, acid 19, 51
—, alcohol-soluble 32
— arises by dehydrogenation 76
—, aromatic constitution for 57
—, aromatic nature of 59
—, artificial 61, 108
—, benzylalcohol groups in 76
—, benzylether groups in 76
—, beech 110, 112
—, benzyl aryl ether in 93
—, biosynthetic 81
—, biphenyl bonds in 102
—, birch 27
—, branching 106
—, bromination of 58
—, C_9 basis 65
—, ^{14}C incorporated in 27, 99—102
—, characteristics of a preparation of 70
—, ^{14}C-labelled compounds incorporated into 17
Lignin, C-methyl content of 61
—, concept of 114
—, cuproxam 51
—, deuterated artificial 108
—, elemental analyses 69
—, ether linkages in 57, 95
—, — oxygen in 75
—, expression of analyses 65
—, formaldehyde from 57, 60
— formation 28, 29, 32—34, 37
— fraction 28
—, glucose incorporated in 27
— grafted onto carbohydrates 93
—, guaiacyl nuclei of 27
—, hydrochloric acid 51
—, hydrogenation of 62
—, hydrolysis of the fraction 96
—, Klason 20, 21, 64
—, mercuration 59
—, methyl 54, 67
—, milled-wood 52
—, native 4, 52
—, oxidation level of 74, 84
—, L-phenylalanine incorporated into 28, 101
— precursor 13, 28
—, protolignin 4, 32, 52
—, refraction index 60
—, rotting of 115
—, schematic model of the constitution of spruce 102
—, sequence in 106
—, shikimic acid incorporated into 27
—, soluble 4, 52
—, spruce 11—13, 27
—, stoichiometric nitration 59
—, sulfonated 13
—, thermoplasticity 51
—, thioglycolic acid 54, 68
—, *p*-toluenesulfonate 57
—, ultraviolet absorption of 60
—, Urban's 57
Lignite 115
Lignols 85, 86
Lignothioglycolic acid 54, 68
Lipids 34, 36
Lolium multiflorum 19
— *perenne* 19
— *temulentum* 19
Lubanol benzoate 83
Lupinus luteus 19, 25
Lycopodium 112
— *obscurum* 113
Lycopods 3, 113

DL-Mandelic acid-2-^{14}C 25
Mäule test 4

Maple 27
Mechanism, carboxyl-activating 31
Medicago sativum 113
Melilotus officinalis 18, 25
Mercuric acetate 59
Mesoid forms 95
Mesomeric radical 75, 85, 86
Metabolic pool 28
Metabolites, aromatic secondary 33
—, primary 34—36
—, secondary 34—36
Metahemipinic acid from labelled DHP 100
— — from lignin grown with labelled coniferin 101
— — — — — — — phenylalanine 101
Methanol, elimination of 71
Methione-$^{14}CH_3$ 31
L-Methionine-methyl-^{14}C 31
Methoxybenzenecarboxylic acids 78
m-Methoxycinnamic acid 28
— acid-β-^{14}C 26
3-Methoxy-4-hydroxytoluene-7-^{14}C 23
Methoxyl content 49, 50
—, deficit of 77, 82
— groups 28
Methylation 12, 31, 76
— reaction 33
Methyltransferase 37
O-Methyltransferase 31
Microorganisms 15, 17
Microsomes 16
Mistletoe 113, 114
Molecule, branching in 106
Molecular layer of lignin 59
Monocotyledons 12, 114
Monolignols 85
Mosses 112, 113
Mung beans seedlings 16, 17
Mutant 35, 36
—, nutritional 15
— strain 36
Mutation 36

Nerine bowdenii 31
Neutral permanganate 12
N-Isovanillyl-tyramine 31
Nitrobenzene-*m*-sulfonate 12
Nitrobenzene 12
— oxidation 28, 61
Nitrogen dioxide 59
Nomenclature of cinnamyl alcohols 55
Norbelladine 31
Nucleic acids 34, 36

Oligolignols 53, 85, 91
—, higher 91
Ontogenesis 98
β-Oxidation 33
Oxidation after methylation 76, 78
—, alkaline copper 12
—, — nitrobenzene 12, 61
— level 84
—, nitrobenzene 11, 13, 61
α-Oxo acid 16
α-Oxoglurarate 17
Oxygen balance 105
—, ether 72
—, total 72

Palms 114
Pampas grass 31
Paper chromatography 14
Pathway, acetate 27
—, biosynthetic 35, 37
Peas 16
— seedlings 16
Peat moss 113
"Per cent conversion" 13
Peroxidase 32, 37, 83
Petunia 31, 33
Phenolase 14, 30, 31
Phenolic compounds 14, 36, 37
— hydroxyl groups 71
Phenols 14
Phenoloxidases 14
Phenylalanine 15—17, 27—37, 100, 101
— ammonia-lyase 30, 31
—, *m*-fluoro 30
—, *p*-fluoro 30
—, *m*-hydroxy 30
—, hydroxylation of 16
—, labelled 29
— pools 16, 29
—, ring-substituted 30
—, transamination of 17
DL-Phenylalanine-β-^{14}C 19, 100, 101
DL-Phenylalanine-α-^{14}C 19. 100, 101
L-Phenylalanine 15, 28, 100, 101
—, generally-labelled 29, 100, 101
Phenylalanine-^{14}C 27, 100, 101
DL-Phenylalanine-$^{14}CHNH_2$ 100
L-Phenylalanine-G-^{14}C 11, 18, 19, 100, 101
— ammonia-lyase 15, 30
Phenylglyceric acids 28
DL-*Threo*-Phenylglyceric acid-β-^{14}C 25
DL-Phenylhydracrylic acid-β-^{14}C 23
DL-*Erythro*-Phenylglyceric acid-β-^{14}C 26
Phenylhydroxylase 37
D-Phenyllactic acid-β-^{14}C 20, 23, 26
L-Phenyllactic acid-β-^{14}C 20
Phenylpropane derivatives 12
— skeleton 12
Phenylpropanoid compounds 12, 13, 16, 28, 32—34
Phenylpyruvate 17, 33

Phenylpyruvic acid-β-^{14}C 20
Phleum pratense 32
Phlobaphenes 48
Phloroglucinol 3
— in hydrochloric acid 98
Phloroglucinol-HCl test 32
Phosphoenolpyruvate 17
Photosynthesis 29
Photosynthetic assimilation 27
Phylogenesis 98
Picea ajanensis 20, 23
Picea excelsa 19, 22—26, 51
Picea pungens 20, 23
— *mariana* 21
Pinoresinol 87
Pinus strobus (tissue cultures) 18, 19, 21, 23, 24, 28
Pittosporum crassifolia 21
Plant enzymes 14
— tissue cultures 11
Plants, administration to 28
—, higher 17, 36
Poa trivialis 19
Polylignols 85
— on surface of polysaccharides 93
Polymer 32
Polymeric natural compounds 48
Polymerization 28
—, peroxidative 32
Polysaccharides 14, 50
—, cell wall 12
—, polylignols on the surface of 93
Polytrichum 113
Polyvinylpyrrolidine 14
Populus balsamifera 18, 22, 25
— *tremuloides* 21
Precursor 10, 28
—, ^{14}C-labelled 17
— of lignin 13, 27
Prediction by the model 107
Prephenic acid 15—17
Proanthocyanidins 50
Protein 12, 14, 28, 34, 36, 50
Protocatechuic acid 58
— —, (carboxyl-labelled) 22, 24
Protolignin 4, 32
Psalliota campestris 83
Psilophytales 34
Pulvinic dilactone 33
Pungenin 11, 33
Pyruvate 17

Quercetin 11
Quinate 17
Quinate-^{14}C 16
Quinate-NAD oxidoreductase 17
Quinic acid 16, 17, 28
Quinic acid, C-labelled 16
Quinone methide 87
— — addition of coniferyl alcohol to the dimeric 91
— —, half-life of 87
— —, rate of reactivity with hydroxy compounds 94

Racemoid forms 95
Radical, aroxyl 85
—, half-life of 86
—, mesomeric 75, 85, 86
Reaction, free radical 34
—, indophenol 71
Rearrangements, allylic 61
Reduction 31
Residue, acetone-insoluble 29
—, bifunctional molecular 50
— extractive-free 25
Rosa wichuraiana 19
Rose plants 16
Russula delica 83
Rutin 11

***S**accharum officinarum* 18, 20
Salix amygdaloides 18, 25
Salvia splendens 16, 20, 23, 26
Scirpus validus 18, 25
Scarlet sage 16
Secale cereale 19
Sequence 103, 106
Sequoia sempervirens 19
Shikimate 17
— NADP oxidoreductase 16
Shikimic acid 10, 15—17, 27, 28, 33, 37
— — -G-^{14}C 18
— —, labelled with ^{14}C 16
— — pathway 27, 33
— — -2,6-^{14}C 18
Siamese benzoin 83
Sinapic acid 28, 31, 32
— acid-β-^{14}C 22, 26
— acid-α-^{14}C 22, 23
Sinapyl alcohol 32, 34, 55, 70
Smilacina stellata 18, 25
Sodium aminoethoxide, titration with 94
— pyruvate 27
Sparganium multipedunculatum 18, 25
Spectroscopy, mass 85
— N. M. R. 108
Sphagnum 114
Spinach 14, 16
Spreading experiment 59
Spruce 12, 28, 30—32
— lignin 12, 13
—, schematic model of the constitution of spruce lignin 102

Stereochemistry 50
Starch 50
Stilbenes 33
Sugar cane 29, 30
Sulfonic acids 13
Syringa vulgaris 19
Syringaldehyde 12, 18—28
Syringic acid (carboxyl-labelled) 22
Syringin 98, 100
Syringoyl methyl ketone 23
Syringyl 28
—, derivatives 13
—, groups 4
— nuclei 28
—, units 28

Tannins 14
Taxonomic distribution 30
— groups 30
Terphenylquinone intermediate 33
Thermoplasticity 51
Thioglycolic acid 54
Timberline 99
Timothy grass 32
Tissue cultures 27, 28
p-Toluenesulfinic acid 57
Tracer 37
— studies 10
Tracheids 3, 6, 34
Transaminase 17
Transamination 17
Transesterification 33
Transpiration 10
Trilignols 91
Triglochin maritima 18, 25
Trimethoxybenzene series, compounds of 80
Trimethylgallic acid (carboxyl-labelled) 24
Tris hydroxymethyl aminomethane buffer 14
Triticum 31
— *aestivum* 16, 18—26
Trytophan 15
L-Tryptophan 15
Tsuga heterophylla 16
Tyrase 30
Tyrosine 12, 15, 16, 27—30, 32, 37
— ammonia-lyases 37
—, C-labelled 15
— pool 16, 29
—, transamination of 17
L-Tyrosine 14, 15, 30
—, (generally labelled) 23
L-Tyrosine-G-^{14}C 20, 23, 25
L-Tyrosine ammonia-lyase (tyrase) 14, 15, 30

Ulmus campestris 19
Unit, sequence of the individual 103, 106
Units large entities glued together by 93

Vanillic acid (carboxyl-labelled) 23
Vanillin 11, 13, 18—28
— (carbonyl-labelled) 24
— (carbonyl-^{14}C) D-glucoside 22
— (carbonyl-^{14}C) L-glucoside 24
— (carboxyl-labelled) 22
—, oxidation to 61
Vanilloyl methyl ketone 11
Vanillyl alcohol (carbinol-^{14}C) 23
Vascular plants 3, 14—17, 30, 33, 34, 36
Veratric acid (carboxyl-labelled) 25
Veratryl aldehyde (carbonyl-labelled) 25
— alcohol (carbinol-labelled) 25
Viscum album 114
Volucrisporin 33

Wheat 16, 17, 27, 31, 32
Wood cellulose 60
—, fossilized 115
—, meals 12
— —, methylated 12
Wound reaction 11

X-ray diagram of wood and jute 60
Xylem 3
Xylitol, uniformly-labelled 27

Zinnia elegans 18, 23

Type-setting and printing: Carl Ritter & Co., Wiesbaden

Molecular Biology, Biochemistry and Biophysics
Molekularbiologie, Biochemie und Biophysik

Volumes published:

Vol. 1 J. H. VANT' HOFF: Imagination in Science. Translation and Introduction by G. F. SPRINGER. VI, 18 pages 8 vo. With 1 portrait. Soft cover binding DM 6,60 / US $ 1.65

Forthcoming volumes:

Vol. 3 T. ROBINSON: The Biochemistry of Alkaloids. X, 149 pages 8 vo. With 37 figures Bound DM 39,— / US $ 9.75

Vol. 4 A. S. SPIRIN and L. P. GAVRILOVA: The Ribosome (in press)

Vol. 5 B. JIRGENSONS: Optical Rotatory Dispersion of Proteins and other Macromolecules (in press)

Vol. 6 F. EGAMI and K. NAKAMURA: Microbial Ribonucleases. Approx. 106 pages 8 vo. With 5 figures. Bound DM 28,— / US $ 7.—

Vol. 7 F. HAWKES: Nucleic Acids and Cytology. Approx. 288 pages 8 vo. With approx. 14 figures. Bound DM 58,— / US $ 14.50

Volumes being planned:

ABELES, R. H., and W. S. BECK: The Mechanism of Action of (Cobamide) Vitamin B_{12} Coenzymes

AIDA, Kô: Amino Acid Fermentation

ANDO, T.: Protamines

ANKER, H. S.: Studies on the Mechanism and Control of Fatty Acid Biosynthesis

ANTONINI, E.: Kinetic Structures and Mechanism of Hemoproteins

BEERMANN, W.: Puffs and their Function in Developmental Biology

BREUER, H., and K. DAHM: Mode of Action of Estrogens

BRILL, A. S.: The Role of Heavy Metals in Biological Oxidation Processes

BURNS, R. C., and R. W. F. HARDY: Nitrogen Fixation in Bacteria and Higher Plants

CALLAN, H. G.: Lampbrush Chromosomes

CHAPMAN, D.: Molecular Biological Aspects of Lipids in Membranes

CHICHESTER, C. O., H. YOKOYAMA and T. O. M. NAKAYAMA: Biosynthesis of Carotenoids

DUMONDE, D. C.: Cell and Tissue Antigens

DUS, K. M.: Analysis of Proteins

ELEY, D. D.: Biological Materials as Semi-Conductors

FENDER, D. H.: Problems of Visual Perception

GIBSON, I.: Paramecium Aurelia and Cytoplasmic Factors

Volumes being planned:

Gibson, Q. H.: Rapid Reactions in Biochemistry

Grecz, N.: Molecular Radiation Biophysics

Grubb, R.: Genetical and Medical Aspects of Immunoglobulin Differentiation

Guillemin, R.: Hypothalamic Releasing Factors

Haugaard, N., and E. Haugaard: Mechanism of Action of Insulin

Heinz, E. and W. Wilbrandt: Biological Transports

Hoffmann-Ostenhof, O.: Biochemistry of the Inositols

Hofmann, Th.: Chymotrypsin and other Serine Proteinases

Jardetzky, O.: Nuclear Magnetic Resonance in Molecular Biology,

Jollès, P., and A. Paraf: Biological and Chemical Basis of Adjuvants

Kleinschmidt, A. K., and D. Lang: A Manual for Electron Microscopy of Nucleic Acid Molecules

Klenk, E.: Cerebrosides, Gangliosides and other Glycolipids

Larner, J.: Chemistry of Hereditary Disease

Ludwick, T. M., J. E. Gander and R. Jenness: Biosynthesis of Milk

Lukens, R. J.: Chemistry of Fungicides

Matthews, M. B.: Molecular Evolution of Connective Tissue

Matthaei, J. H.: Protein Biosynthesis

Maurer, P. H.: Chemical and Structural Basis of Antigenicity

McManus, T. J.: Red Cell Ion Transport and Related Metabolic Processes

Middleton, J. T., and J. B. Mudd: Air Pollution

Nelson, R. A.: The Complement System. Physicochemical Characterization and Biologic Reactivities

Okunuki, K.: Cytochromes

Osborn, M. J., and L. Rothfield: Bacterial Cell Wall Synthesis and Function

Porath, J.: Modern Methods of Separation of Proteins and other Macromolecules

Quastel, J. H.: Chemical Control of Cell Metabolism and Function

Reeves, P.: Bacteriocins

Runnström, J.: Molecular Biology of the Fertilization Process

Schanne, O., and Elena Ruiz de Ceretti: Impedance Measurements in Biological Cells

Seliger, H. H.: Bioluminescence

Shulman, S., and F. Milgrom: Organ Specificity

Stadtman, E. R.: Enzymatic Regulation of Metabolism

Vinnikov, J. A.: Principles of Structural, Chemical and Functional Organization of Sensory Receptors

Wallenfels, K., and H. Rickenberg: Beta-Galactosidase: Structure, Biochemical Genetics and Function of an Enzyme

Werle, E.: Plasma Kinines

Yagi, K.: Biochemistry of Flavins

Zweifach, B. W.: Shock